PENGUIN CANADA

WEEKDAY WONDERS

Bestselling cookbook author, registered nutritional consultant, newspaper columnist, product spokesperson, owner of the Rose Reisman Cooking School, caterer, television personality, and mother of four, Rose Reisman has spent her career helping Canadians enjoy healthier, more delicious food. Rose, a regular guest on radio and television, conducts seminars and workshops on living and eating well. She is also a major supporter of breast cancer research and treatment, and has raised more than $1 million for the cause through the sales of her books. *Weekday Wonders* is her fourteenth book.

Also by Rose Reisman

The Complete Idiot's Guide® to Light Desserts

The Art of Living Well

Divine Indulgences

Sensationally Light Pasta and Grains

Rose Reisman's Light Vegetarian Cooking

Rose Reisman's Enlightened Kitchen (cookbook and video)

Rose Reisman's Enlightened Home Cooking

Rose Reisman Brings Home Light Pasta

Rose Reisman Brings Home Light Cooking

Rose Reisman Brings Home Pasta Dishes

Rose Reisman Brings Home Spa Desserts

Manhattan's Dessert Scene

The Dessert Scene

rose reisman

weekday wonders
healthy light meals for every day

PENGUIN
CANADA

PENGUIN CANADA

Penguin Group (Canada), a division of Pearson Penguin Canada Inc., 10 Alcorn Avenue, Toronto, Ontario M3C 2T8

Penguin Group (U.K.), 80 Strand, London WC2R 0RL, England
Penguin Group (U.S.), 375 Hudson Street, New York, New York 10014, U.S.A.
Penguin Group (Australia) Inc., 250 Camberwell Road, Camberwell, Victoria 3124, Australia
Penguin Group (Ireland), 25 St. Stephen's Green, Dublin 2, Ireland
Penguin Books India (P) Ltd, 11, Community Centre, Panchsheel Park, New Delhi – 110 017, India
Penguin Group (New Zealand), cnr Rosedale and Airborne Roads, Albany, Auckland 1310, New Zealand
Penguin Books (South Africa) (Pty) Ltd, 24 Sturdee Avenue, Rosebank 2196, South Africa

Penguin Group, Registered Offices: 80 Strand, London WC2R 0RL, England
First published 2004

 2 3 4 5 6 7 8 9 10 (WEB)

Manufactured in Canada.

National Library of Canada Cataloguing in Publication
Reisman, Rose, 1953–
    Weekday wonders : healthy light meals for every day / Rose Reisman.
Includes index.
ISBN 0-14-301615-6

    1. Low-fat diet—Recipes. 2. Quick and easy cookery. I. Title.
RM237.7.R473   641.5'638   C2003-906530-8

Visit the Penguin Group (Canada) website at **www.penguin.ca**
Visit Rose Reisman on the web at **www.rosereisman.com**

No matter how many books I write, my dedication will always be to
my wonderful family, who are my daily lifeline.

Sam, my incredibly supportive husband, a.k.a. "the Wildman!"
He adds energy to my day.

Natalie, my wonderful, highly independent daughter who is a going concern for anyone around her.
David, the most balanced man I've ever met. He's off to university this year and I'll miss him dearly.
Laura, the "active" teenager who has matured into a wonderful and respectable young lady.
Adam, my "baby," who is slowly leaving his childhood and yet who is growing up much too fast.
And to the peaceful times in my day courtesy of my "animal house."
Love to Aspen, Meiko, Misty, and Ozzie!

contents

acknowledgments

Thanks to the wonderful assistants in my kitchen whom I could never have done without:
Eva Mollar, Lily Lim, Mila Doloricon, and Joanna Trim.

Thanks to Lesleigh Landry who helped edit the recipes and Roxanna Roberts for the nutritional analyses.

Thanks to the team at Penguin who always make my job so easy:
Nicole de Montbrun, Andrea Crozier, Ed Carson, Tracy Bordian, Sarah Weber, and Karen McMullin.

Thanks to Per Christiansen for the beautiful cover photograph and Mary Opper for her lovely cover and interior design.

Thanks to my wonderful friends Kathy Kacer and Susan Gordin for their honest opinion of many of the recipes and for helping me to formulate some of the practical ideas in *Weekday Wonders*.

Canadian Breast Cancer Foundation®

Dear Reader:

The Canadian Breast Cancer Foundation (CBCF) is very fortunate to, once again, be the recipient of generous support from Rose Reisman. The sale of Rose's newest cookbook, *Weekday Wonders,* is one of the countless ways Rose has demonstrated her leadership in the fight against breast cancer. By purchasing this collection of wonderful recipes, you are making the difference and helping us eradicate breast cancer as a life-threatening disease.

As the leading national volunteer-based organization dedicated to the fight against breast cancer, the Canadian Breast Cancer Foundation works collaboratively to fund, support, and advocate for:

- relevant and innovative breast cancer research
- meaningful education and awareness programs
- early diagnosis and effective treatment
- a positive quality of life for those living with breast cancer

Since our inception in 1986, CBCF has allocated millions of dollars in grants for breast cancer projects and services. We applaud Rose Reisman and everyone who worked on the winning recipe for putting together this project and helping us create a future without breast cancer.

With sincere thanks,

Carol Seidman, CFRE
CHIEF EXECUTIVE OFFICER
Canadian Breast Cancer Foundation

creating a future without breast cancer

phone 1-800-387-9816

introduction

If your memories of childhood bring to mind a wonderful hot dinner each night with the entire family, consider yourself fortunate! It's a memory few of today's children will have decades from now.

Not so long ago, most moms weren't working full-time outside the home, kids weren't attending umpteen after-school programs, and dads weren't arriving home from work at 8 p.m. night after night. The emphasis at mealtime was to have a wholesome dinner on the table for the family every day of the week. Those were truly *Leave It to Beaver* days.

Not so today! Now, many parents work at high-powered jobs that require long hours and a great deal of commitment. Even if they aren't travelling or entertaining clients, many working parents still don't get home by 6 p.m. When they do arrive home early, often they are just in time to take the kids off to a hockey practice, dance class, swimming lesson, or another of the myriad activities most kids are involved in after school. As well, increasingly in today's families, a single parent must shoulder all of these responsibilities.

The notion of a family dinner hour can no longer be taken for granted. If everyone in the family is busy working, doing homework, attending extracurricular activities, and so on, who's doing the cooking? The answer, of course, is no one! That's why fast-food restaurants and takeout eateries are proliferating at an alarming rate. It's no wonder that our country is suffering from increased obesity, Type 2 diabetes, heart problems, and an increased cancer rate.

Why can't we continue living like this? Well, it's simple: living in a fast-paced world eliminates much of the quantity and quality of time we have to spend with our families. The dinner hour is our only hope of catching up with each member of the family and finding out what's going on in their daily lives. Every time I sit down and share a meal with my family, I'm surprised—even shocked—at the amount of detail I learn about my children's lives. (I actually get answers from my kids that are more than two words long.) Even if you do not have a family, sitting down to a homemade dinner with your partner or friends allows you to spend more quality time together.

So, welcome to *Weekday Wonders*—the cookbook you've been waiting for. It features easy, delicious, healthy meals that you can prepare quickly for your family. Each recipe gives preparation and cook times, make-ahead instructions for doing some of the preparation when you have a bit of free time, easy steps, and a nutritional analysis. Most contain tips and suggest ingredient substitutions. And every recipe is guaranteed to be delicious, yet lower in fat, calories, and cholesterol. What more could you want?

weekday wonders

putting the "wonder" into your weekday meals

I've noticed that one of the reasons I enjoy holidays with my family is because life is more relaxed and unstructured then. I also realize that I enjoy spending more time in the kitchen during holidays because people love to gather there. Food always seems to bring us closer together.

So, when the holidays are over, work becomes hectic again, and school schedules make the concept of quality living nearly impossible, how can we try to re-create this quality time? One of the best ways I have discovered is through making the effort to have as many family meals together during the week as possible. If I take a few moments to organize my day, I can actually get a fresh, delicious, healthy meal on the table most nights. Sharing a meal gives my family 30 minutes together, 30 minutes in which we *are* a family.

the importance of mealtime

There are many good reasons to sit down and eat a meal together.

family bonding

The normal day for most people is hectic and busy, and usually leaves no time for family members to bond. In my family, having a family dinner every night is almost impossible because we all have different schedules. Therefore, I plan at least two dinners a week at which we all sit together even if only for 30 minutes. At the kitchen table or in the dining room, we talk about anything and everything—our day, the world, politics, religion—you'd be amazed where the conversation can go. No matter where our lively discussions lead us, they can happen only when we are all at the table "breaking bread" together.

cost

Each time you eat out either at a fast-food restaurant or a full-service establishment, keep your bill. At the end of the month, calculate what you have spent. You will be shocked. No matter where you do it, eating out is expensive. Even a meal at a fast-food restaurant can cost a family of four more than $35. The same dinner would cost about $10 if you made it at home.

healthier and tastier meals

If you are a smart shopper, food made at home is healthier for you than restaurant food and contains fewer preservatives. Most restaurants use an abundance of fat and salt to make their foods taste better. Good home cooking calls for better quality food and only healthy seasonings to make the food taste delicious.

improved health

More than 55 percent of Canada's population is overweight, and it's disturbing to note that there is an epidemic of teenage obesity and an increase in Type 2 diabetes in the younger generation. The health of our nation should be enough to get you and your family motivated to lead a healthier lifestyle, including cooking nutritious food at home. Illness and death due to our poor diet and lifestyle are more prevalent than ever before. Our poor diet has been implicated in 5 of the 10 leading causes of death of adult North Americans—heart disease, stroke, cancer, diabetes, and complications as a result of osteoporosis.

keeping your family healthy

The time you spend cooking at home allows you to teach your family healthy eating habits and introduce new foods. Unquestionably, parents and older siblings are primary role models for children and have a great influence on how they eat and how much they exercise. Of course, there's no guarantee that my four children—who for years have witnessed how my husband and I eat and exercise—will lead a healthier lifestyle, but the chances are good that they will.

obstacles to overcome

Numerous obstacles make healthy eating difficult:

- Fast-food establishments, which dominate every street corner
- Huge food portions, which are all too common in restaurants
- Junk food, and the vending machines that make it available everywhere
- Food labels that can be misleading or difficult to interpret
- The abundance of processed and preserved foods available at the grocery store
- Television, computers, and electronic games, which reduce or eliminate our children's desire and time available to exercise and play
- Overly busy lives, which mean that working parents have less time to cook meals and sit down together with their children at dinner

solutions

If we want our families to be healthier, we have to emphasize good food and exercise. Here are some suggestions to help you do that:

1. Help children develop a healthy attitude to food from an early age.
2. Don't use food as a reward, punishment, or comfort.
3. Don't define food as "good" or " bad."
4. Have healthy fresh food available and encourage your family to snack on these foods.
5. Don't talk obsessively about food, weight, and diets.
6. Promote exercise—keep your family moving.
7. Keep junk food, packaged food, and dining in fast-food restaurants to a minimum.
8. Start cooking "lighter" and healthier meals.
9. Don't allow your family to go hours without eating, which can lead to bingeing and poor eating habits.
10. Organize your day in terms of eating and shopping. Organization is a valuable tool in the fight against poor eating habits.

starting on the path to weekday wonders

Some of you already have begun the journey, but many of you may be just getting your feet wet. Let's assume we share the same goal: we would like to be able to walk in the door at the end of the day and prepare a delicious, healthy weekday dinner with as little effort as possible. It can be done, but you need the right tools:

1. You need some basic knowledge about what constitutes healthy eating and good nutrition. Canada's Food Guide can help you here.
2. You have to develop a personal family strategy for shopping and cooking. Know your weekly time constraints in terms of work and family, and divide up the shopping and cooking chores if possible.
3. You have to organize your meal planning and shopping. You can't just "wing" it!

the new nutrition

Understanding Canada's Food Guide is the key to proper nutrition. Health Canada developed this guide to help Canadians meet their daily nutritional needs and possibly prevent obesity and debilitating diseases such as heart disease, diabetes, and even cancer. Designed to meet the basic nutritional requirements of healthy children and adults, this guide is a good start to improving and adjusting your eating habits to fit your age and activity level.

The foods included in the food guide are low in fat, high in fibre, and loaded with vitamins and minerals. The guide keeps fat and sugar to a minimum and does not eliminate one food group, as do many fad diets today.

The food guide's key strategies are as follows:

- Incorporate a variety of foods from each of the four food groups into your diet.
- Choose the majority of your foods from the grains and vegetables and fruit groups.
- Always select lower-fat foods and leaner meats. Keep foods that are high in saturated fat to a minimum.
- Maintain an ideal body weight and incorporate exercise into your day.
- Limit your intake of coffee, salt, and alcohol.

the four food groups Canada's Food Guide recommends the number of servings you should eat *daily* from each of four food groups:

1. **Grains:** 5 to 12 servings of grain products (1 slice of bread, 1/2 cup rice or pasta)
2. **Vegetables and fruits:** 5 to 10 servings (1 medium fruit, 1 cup leafy vegetables, or 1/2 cup chopped vegetables)
3. **Milk products:** 2 to 4 servings (1 cup lower-fat milk, 3/4 cup lower-fat yogurt, 1-1/2 oz cheese)
4. **Meat and alternatives:** 2 to 3 servings (3 ounces beef, poultry, or fish; 1/2 cup beans)

Remember that the food guide is exactly that—merely a guide, not something written in stone. If you are physically active, naturally you can eat the number of servings toward the higher end of the range given in the food guide. Depending on the type of protein, 3 ounces of protein can contain different amounts of calories and fat. Fatty spareribs contain much more fat and calories than lean fish. You can always enjoy more of the lean protein in your daily intake.

It's best to go through the food guide with a nutritionist who can clearly calculate your daily needs according your specific lifestyle and characteristics.

your personal family strategy

Now that you have some understanding of your nutritional needs, you have to develop a personal strategy for you and your family. Here are some facts to consider:

- What foods does your family enjoy most?
- Who's going to do the shopping and cooking?

- Do you want to organize your weekday meals on a weekly or semi-weekly schedule, or do you prefer to cook fresh daily?
- Do you want to have "backup" meals in the freezer? When is the best time to prepare these?

Once you can answer these important questions, you can begin to organize your weekday meals with success and satisfaction.

organization: steps on the path to weekday wonders

Imagine what your life would be like if you went to business meetings unprepared, or if you didn't keep track of your children's schedule for various weekly programs, or if you missed social or professional engagements. Life would become quite chaotic and disorganized, as would your home and your meal planning. It's pretty hard to eat healthy weekday meals if the shopping hasn't been done or the pantry and freezer are poorly stocked.

Although most of us lead highly structured lives, we fall behind when it comes to structuring simple daily routines. We eat whatever is available or order in for convenience. It's often convenience foods, often junk food, that lead to obesity, high blood pressure, high cholesterol, diabetes, and certain cancers.

Following these four simple steps will help you get organized:

1. **Plan your grocery shopping and meal preparation, whether you do these tasks daily, semi-weekly, or weekly.** The greatest problem in daily meal preparation is thinking about it too late, on the drive home, for instance. If your kitchen is not well stocked, you can forget about making a healthy meal once you park your car in the driveway.

   Decide in advance when and how to plan your meals and when best to shop for the week. The weekend is truly the best time to plan your next week's meals. Decide what your family enjoys and actually select the meals for the next few days or the week.

   If you know you may have a couple of busier weeks, you might consider making extra meals on the weekend and freezing them.

2. **Make a list of the groceries you'll need for the week.** Post your shopping list where you can always add to it. List the ingredients you'll need to buy for the recipes you plan to make. Always keep basic ingredients on hand.

3. **Order in your groceries if you don't have time to shop.** One of the greatest discoveries for me has been home-delivery grocery shopping. I order in large quantities because of the size of my family and my entertaining habits. But for the average person, getting a small quantity of all the products you use on a regular basis saves you time and money. Another benefit of home delivery: your back doesn't hurt from carrying around those groceries and household items week after week!

Although I like to buy my own produce and dairy products, grocery-delivery companies will also select these items for you if you don't have the time.

I often order larger quantities of meats and fish from distributors at better prices and quality than the average supermarket provides. If you cook daily, it's always wise to have fish or meat in the freezer. If you have a family of four or more, consider putting an extra fridge and freezer in the basement or laundry room. You'll be shocked at how quickly you'll fill it. You might be able to arrange for your neighbourhood store to deliver to your home.

4. **Have someone else do the cooking.** Nowadays, cooking services are available that will cook a week's worth of dinner and lunch meals. These services either cook at their facility or come to your home during the day to cook, package, and freeze a variety of meals, which often are reasonably priced.

supermarkets

Today's supermarkets, or "superstores," are so much more than just grocery stores. They include specialized food markets, equipment such as cooking utensils, drugstores, camera shops, and nurseries. I find shopping in these big stores an exhilarating experience. They often feature new and specialty foods.

Of course, it's important to know how to shop properly and to be aware of the false or misleading claims some companies put on their product labels.

labelling as a second language Trying to understand product labels is like trying to understand a second language. Never make a food choice based on a product label or marketing campaign. It is important to read between the lines and know what the terms producers use really mean. A food labelled "light" or "low in cholesterol" or one said to contain "no fat" can still be filled with calories and other ingredients that can be harmful to your health. Examine the calories, saturated fat, cholesterol, sodium, and fibre content listed on the label, and make sure that they are within your guidelines for healthy eating.

Today, many product claims seem designed to confuse the consumer. Usually, such confusion is intended to make a product look healthier for you and more appealing than it actually is. You might see products claims such as "no fat," "no cholesterol," "lite," or "light"—and many others. Below are some interpretations of the most common food labelling claims.

anything-free Many labels include the word "free": fat free, calorie free, cholesterol free, sodium free. What these terms indicate is that one serving of the food contains such a small amount of the substance that it doesn't mean much in the nutritional picture and you don't have to be concerned about it.

Here are what some common terms amount to:

Term/Amount (per 100 gram serving)

Fat free	Less than 0.5 gram
Calorie free	Less than 1 calorie
Sodium free	No more than 5 milligrams
Cholesterol free	No more than 3 milligrams

light or lite These terms can be confusing and misleading. When "light" refers to a food product that has been altered, the term means that the food contains one-third fewer calories or half the fat of the regular product. "Lite" can be used to describe the taste, color, or texture of the food in which *the fat or calories remain the same*—so "lite" olive oil may be light in taste, texture, or simply color. "Light sodium" means a product contains half the amount of sodium used to make the regular product.

low or reduced The word "low" on a label tells you that the product has a reduced level of a specific ingredient. Be aware that a product low in fat may still be high in calories, or vice versa. "Reduced" compares the product with the regular product.

Term/Amount (per 100 gram serving)

Low fat	3 grams or less
Low (in) cholesterol	No more than 20 milligrams
Low calorie	15 calories or less
Low in saturated fat	No more than 2 grams
Low sodium	Less than 40 milligrams; less than 50 percent of the sodium in the regular product
Fat reduced	At least 25 percent less fat than in the regular product
Calorie reduced	50 percent fewer calories than in the regular product

source This word indicates that the food product provides a significant amount of a nutrient, say, fibre.

Term/Amount (per 100 gram serving)

Good source of fibre	2 grams
High source of fibre	4 grams
Very high source of fibre	6 grams

Since the Recommended Daily Intake (RDI) for fibre is 25 to 35 grams, you can see that even a very high source of fibre provides only a part of what you need every day. Nutrient sources are defined as follows:

- A high source must provide 20 percent or more of the RDI for that nutrient.
- A good source must contain between 10 percent and 19 percent of the RDI for that nutrient.

Here are some other terms you may see on product labels:

fresh The food is raw, has never been frozen, has never been heated, and contains no preservatives.

fortified or enriched The food has a nutrient added to it so that at least 10 percent of the RDI for that nutrient is present. For example, if a food is fortified with iron, then 10 percent of the iron you need in your daily intake is in one serving of this food.

healthy This term is not always used appropriately. It means that the food is low in fat and saturated fat, and that a serving does not contain more than 480 milligrams of sodium or more than 60 milligrams of cholesterol.

lean and extra lean These terms refer to the fat content of meat, fish, and chicken. Lean food has fewer than 10 grams of fat, 4 grams of saturated fat, and 95 milligrams of cholesterol per 100 gram serving. Extra lean food contains fewer than 5 grams of fat, 2 grams of saturated fat, and 85 milligrams of cholesterol.

natural or organic These terms are also used loosely. When applied to meat or poultry and used accurately, they refer to food that is minimally processed and free of artificial ingredients. For other foods, these terms have no legal definition. Fruits and vegetables bearing these designations have been grown with virtually no pesticides or chemicals.

100% pure fruit juice Fruit juice labelling can be misleading. To be 100 percent fruit juice, juice must contain nothing but fruit. Juice labelled "pure fruit juice" can have only 10 percent to 34 percent fruit content. The rest is made up of water, sugar, color, and flavoring. Fruit-flavored drinks have only 10 percent real fruit juice or none at all. Read the labels carefully.

When you are reading a food label, pay attention to the order of the ingredients on the ingredients list. The first ingredient listed is the one with the most volume by weight in the food. Therefore, if the first ingredient is a form of fat, you know that the product consists mainly of fat. If the label emphasizes whole wheat flour, look at the order of the ingredients to see whether sugar or fat is the first ingredient and the whole wheat flour is toward the end of the list. The ingredients in most food products are categorized and worded on product labels as described in the following paragraphs.

fat This can be listed as butter, lard, vegetable shortening, hydrogenated vegetable oil, or partially hydrogenated oil. "All vegetable oil" on the label does not mean that the food contains no cholesterol or is low in fat. The fat could be hydrogenated or saturated, for instance, as in the case of palm or coconut oil.

sugar This can be listed as sucrose, glucose, dextrose, fructose, maltose, lactose, honey, corn syrup, or molasses. If a label says "no added sugar," the product may still be high in natural sugar, for example, from fruit.

sodium This can be listed as salt, onion salt, celery salt, garlic salt, monosodium glutamate (MSG), baking powder, baking soda, benzoate, sodium citrate, or sodium phosphate. MSG is also known as hydrolyzed vegetable protein. Note that a food such as bouillon is high in sodium.

flour products This listing can cause confusion. We know that the best flour for us is whole wheat flour, but often the terms on labels are misleading. For instance, if just "wheat flour" is listed, it means that the white flour is mixed with some whole wheat flour.

food additives The topic of additives is one of the most confusing areas of all. We have been led to believe that any food product that contains an additive must be harmful to our health. Often, we assume that any additive name that we can't pronounce must be bad for us. But some additives actually enhance the nutritional quality of a food. For example, vitamins and minerals are added to enrich foods such as grains, milk, juices, soy products, and other products. The way to minimize your intake of additives is to eat fresh or minimally processed foods as much as possible. Processed foods always contain the most additives.

These are the better additives:

calcium propionate This additive supplies some calcium and retards spoilage caused by bacteria, particularly in breads.

beta carotene This adds nutrition and a yellow or orange color to foods such as margarine and cheeses. Remember that this nutrient is also a powerful antioxidant.

monoglycerides and diglycerides These maintain the smooth or soft consistency of foods, such as margarine, ice cream, and breads.

vitamin E This antioxidant is added to oils.

vitamins and minerals These replace nutrients that are lost when food is processed.

emulsifiers and stabilizers These include lecithin, carrageenan, and guar gum. They are used to prevent foods such as peanut butter from separating and to improve the consistency and texture of products.

citric acid/pH control agents These additives prevent botulism in low-acid canned goods.

These additives are questionable or undesirable:

BHT and BHA Found in gum, active yeast, and processed foods, these additives are used to prevent spoilage. BHT and BHA can cause increased cholesterol levels, allergic reactions, liver and kidney damage, and loss of vitamin D.

sulfites Also known as sulfur dioxide, sodium sulfite, and sodium bisulfite, sulfites are used, especially at restaurant salad bars, to make vegetables look fresher and to prevent discoloration. Sulfites are also found in canned food, dehydrated food, processed cookies and crackers, frozen shrimp, and wine. They can cause allergic reactions and worsen asthma in some people.

nitrates and nitrites Commonly found in deli smoked meats and preserved meats, these additives are used to maintain color, minimize bacteria, and enhance flavor and have been linked to headaches, cancer, and birth defects.

artificial colors Red, yellow, blue, and green colorants are used to enhance color and usually are found in lower-nutrient foods, such as candy and soft drinks. These additives are still under review.

artificial sweeteners These are used in soft drinks, yogurts, and ice creams and are sold in packages as beverage sweeteners. Some artificial sweeteners, used in moderation, pose no serious health risk.

monosodium glutamate MSG is found in additives termed hydrolyzed or textured protein, sodium and calcium caseinate, yeast extract, autolyzed yeast, and gelatin. MSG is a very common additive that modifies the taste and aroma of food without adding color or smell. It is found in canned soups and vegetables, sauces, snacks, frozen foods, and seasonings. This additive is most commonly known to be used in Asian food to enhance flavor and give a salty taste. Common side effects of eating MSG include headaches, a numb sensation in the neck and down the spine, and/or tightness in the chest.

Now that you understand what a product label means, let's go shopping.

vegetables and fruits section In the past decade, enormous research has been done on diets rich in fruits and vegetables and how they may be responsible for lowering the risk of various cancers, high blood pressure, cholesterol levels, intestinal disorders such as constipation and diverticulosis, osteoporosis, and macular degeneration, which can cause blindness. These foods supply the majority of vitamins and minerals we need to live a healthy life. They supply antioxidants; vitamins A, C, and K; and beta carotene, folate, and potassium. Fruits and vegetables contain phytochemicals, which are health-promoting compounds found in plants that help protect them; when we eat these foods, the same compounds protect our bodies against disease.

dairy products aisle On an outside aisle of the supermarket, you'll usually find the dairy products. According to Canada's Food Guide, you should consume between two and four servings of dairy products a day. One serving of dairy equals 1 cup milk, 3/4 cup yogurt, 1-1/2 ounces natural cheese, or 2 ounces sliced processed cheese.

Always buy dairy products with the latest expiration date so that they will stay fresh longer once you get them home. All milk and dairy products are labelled with a milk fat (MF) or butter fat (BF) percentage. Naturally, the lower the number, the lower the fat content. What can be confusing is that 2% milk may contain only 2 percent fat by weight but 35 percent of its total calories may come from fat. About 23 percent of the total calories in 1% milk are from fat.

Other milk products you should include in your shopping basket for lower-fat cooking are buttermilk and 2% evaporated milk. A lower-fat diet should always minimize full-fat dairy products of any kind, such as cream cheese, whipping cream, cheese, and sour cream. Many lower-fat alternatives are available today. Avoid non-dairy creamers or fake whipped toppings. They are made from hydrogenated vegetable fat, which is a form of saturated fat.

milk Milk is important for supplying calcium and vitamin D. Varieties of milk range from homogenized 3% MF milk to 2% MF, 1% MF, skim, and non-fat milk. I always avoid homogenized milk and select milk with 2 percent MF or less. For cooking purposes, I like to use either 1% or 2% milk.

Let's look at the fat and calories per 1 cup serving:

Milk	Calories	Fat (grams)	Calcium (milligrams)
Homogenized	150	8	200
2% MF	125	5	315
1% MF	105	2	315
Skim	90	1	315

sour cream Sour cream is great for sauces, dips, and toppings. The usual fat content is 14 percent MF, but you can now find sour cream with from 0 percent to 5 percent MF, which is creamy and delicious—perfect for baking and cooking purposes.

cheese Let's look at the varieties of cheeses:

- Very hard cheeses include Parmesan, Romano, and Asiago.
- Hard cheeses include Cheddar, Swiss, and Gruyère.
- Soft cheeses include brick, Havarti, Brie, mozzarella, blue, and Camembert.
- Unripened cheeses include cottage, cream, goat and feta, pot, and fresh ricotta.

The soft cheeses can be found in lower-fat forms. For example, cottage cheese can be found in forms containing 0.5 percent to 2 percent MF. Ricotta cheese can now be found that contains as little as 5 percent MF. The fat content of cream cheeses in Canada has been reduced to approximately 25 percent MF from the original 35 percent MF.

When buying hard or natural cheeses such as mozzarella, Swiss, and Cheddar, select those lower in MF. Regular whole-fat cheeses can have anywhere from 24 percent MF to 35 percent MF. The best-tasting lower-fat cheeses will have anywhere from 10 percent MF to 15 percent MF. They are also great to cook with. The taste and texture of the lowest fat cheeses, with less than 5 percent MF, usually are inferior, and these cheeses are not good to cook with.

yogurt More nutritious than milk, yogurt contains more calcium, approximately 350 milligrams per cup (compared with 315 milligrams for 1% milk). Fruit yogurts are less nutritious than plain yogurt since fruit yogurts contain less yogurt and more sugar. Lower-fat yogurts are good, but they are often loaded with sugar, so read the labels. The artificially sweetened ones are lower in calories but have chemical sweeteners that are not good for you. Your best bet is to have low-fat plain yogurt and add your own fresh or dried fruit.

eggs Eggs are a good source of protein, iron, and vitamin A, but they do contain saturated fat and cholesterol. All the cholesterol is found in the yolk, which can have more than 200 milligrams of cholesterol with 5 grams of fat. Since the RDI for cholesterol is only 320 milligrams, many people restrict their weekly intake of eggs.

Egg whites are cholesterol free, and one egg white has only 15 calories. Substitute two egg whites for each whole egg in a recipe, or use an egg substitute. Read the label to ensure that the egg substitute doesn't contain food coloring and chemicals. Some egg substitutes available in stores today are made from 90 percent egg whites and 10 percent egg yolks. The color is just like that of whole egg, the taste is great, and this product is more nutritious than eggs.

To be safe, buy AA- or A-graded eggs from refrigerated cases only. Check the quality of the eggs before you buy them. Never buy cracked or leaking eggs, and never use a cracked egg because it can be contaminated with bacteria such as salmonella, which can cause food poisoning.

Don't be fooled by the color difference between white and brown eggs. Brown eggs have the same nutritional value as white eggs. Often, I buy white and brown eggs and use the white ones for cooking and hard-cook the brown ones.

Omega-3 eggs, containing polyunsaturated fat, are produced by feeding laying hens a special diet containing 10 percent to 20 percent ground flaxseed, which is high in omega-3 fatty acids. These eggs are more heart healthy and help lower the bad (LDL) cholesterol in your blood. Three to four eggs supply the same amount of omega-3 fatty acids as a 3 ounce serving of salmon, but they still contain cholesterol and fat.

grains and cereals aisle According to Canada's Food Guide, per day you may eat from 5 to 12 servings of grains, your complex carbohydrates. This may sound like a lot, but remember that one serving is only 1/2 cup. A plate of pasta, which might consist of 4 cups, equals 8 servings. Grain products include bread, crackers, cereals, rice, pasta, and other grains such as barley, kasha, millet, quinoa, and oats. Starchier vegetables, such as potatoes and sweet potatoes, should be counted as grain—half a regular potato equals one serving.

Whole grains may cut the risk of heart disease, stroke, diabetes, colon cancer, and high blood pressure. Select whole-grain products, which are much healthier for you than white-flour carbohydrates. Whole-grain products are a source of fibre, vitamins, minerals, and phytochemicals, and are also a low-glycemic food, which means that you feel satisfied longer. Always look for the label "whole wheat," which means that 100 percent whole wheat flour has been used. Be careful of the word "wheat" used alone on a product as this word often refers to a combination of whole wheat and white flour.

To determine whether you are obtaining enough fibre in grain products, read the nutritional information. Each slice of bread should contain at least 2 grams of fibre. Per serving, cereals should contain at least 4 grams of fibre, less than 8 grams of sugar, and 2 grams of fat or less.

fats and oils aisle Certain fats, such as monounsaturated and polyunsaturated fats, are actually good for you, helping to lower cholesterol. In general, though, it's wise to limit your consumption of fat because of the calories. Remember, 1 tablespoon of any fat contains about 120 calories and 14 grams of fat! You can see how easily the calories and fat can add up and cause weight gain. When a liquid oil is changed into a solid oil by a process called hydrogenation, trans-fatty acids are the result. The fat has become a saturated fat and causes the damage associated with that kind of fat. When shopping, read the nutrition label and be sure the fat is either monounsaturated or polyunsaturated. Coconut and palm oil, even though vegetable fats, are considered saturated fats. The best oils for you are monounsaturated; use canola, extra virgin olive, and peanut oils for most of your cooking needs. Polyunsaturated oils include corn, safflower, soybean, sesame, and cottonseed oils.

cooking sprays Use these to coat your pans and skillets and thus reduce the amount of fat needed for cooking. These sprays contain few calories and do the trick. (Avoid using the cans near an open flame—it may pose a fire hazard.) If you prefer not to use the store-bought cans, then purchase a pump and fill it with your own oil.

solid fats and oils Lard, vegetable shortening, butter, and margarine are examples of saturated fats. You can buy margarines that are non-hydrogenated and unsaturated. The softer the margarine, the healthier it is for you. Look for a brand that has at least twice as much polyunsaturated as saturated fat.

meat, poultry, and fish section Protein is essential in our diets. It helps maintain blood pressure and water balance, and is needed to transport most substances, such as insulin, in and out of the body's cells. The amount of protein we require in a day is between 50 and 80 grams—the amount contained in 7 to 11 ounces of meat. Allow about 1/4 to 1/3 pound per serving of boneless meat or poultry. If the meat has some bone, then a serving is approximately 1/3 to 1/2 pound per person. When buying meat that has many bony sections, such as ribs, shanks, or shoulder cuts, allow 3/4 to 1 pound per person. Buy about 1/4 to 1/3 pound of fish per person.

During the past 20 years, meat consumption in North America has dropped 28 percent, mostly due to the press about saturated fat and cholesterol leading to heart disease and other diseases. But today, meat is leaner than it's ever been. Certain lean cuts of meat can be as low in fat and cholesterol as chicken or fish.

Pork tenderloin is very low in fat, as are skinless turkey or chicken breast. Turkey breast contains only 5 percent fat calories, even less than chicken at 8 percent fat calories. But if you decide to indulge in chicken or turkey bolognas or franks, then you are getting at least 70 percent fat calories. Remember to remove the skin and trim the fat from all meat—this will lessen the amount of saturated fat by as much as half.

Classifications of meat—AAA, AA, and A—describe its tenderness, juiciness, and flavor. Sometimes you'll also see meat classified as prime, choice, select, good, or standard. The difference is the amount of fat marbling. AAA and prime meat has the most fat and is the tastiest, but not the healthiest for you.

When meat is described as lean, it should contain no more than 10 percent fat when raw. Leaner cuts of meat can be tougher because they contain little fat. Tenderize them by marinating them in vinegar, wine, lemon juice, buttermilk, or yogurt for several hours. Flank steak becomes tender after just two hours of marinating.

beef Select lean cuts such as sirloin, inside round, rump roast, sirloin tip, strip loin, flank, blade, tenderloin, chuck steaks, or roasts. The fattiest cuts are rib roasts, brisket, regular or medium ground beef, and short ribs.

ground beef This is the third-largest source of saturated fat for the average person (after cheese and milk). Ground beef can be labelled 80 percent lean, but that refers to the percentage of fat by weight—20 percent—which contributes 70 percent of the total calories. Try replacing ground beef with ground turkey, chicken, or veal.

lamb and veal Leg of lamb, veal roasts, veal cutlets, veal loin roasts, and veal chops are among the leanest cuts.

pork Pork is 31 percent leaner than it was 10 years ago because of changes in the breeding and feeding practices used in the pork industry. The tenderloin, centre loin chop, lean ham, and loin and rib end roasts are the healthiest choices. The fattiest choices are ribs, loin blade, and shoulder.

poultry Poultry of all kinds is the leanest source of animal protein as long as you remove the skin before eating the meat. It has one-third the fat and calories of red meat. Try boneless and skinless chicken and turkey breast, Cornish hen, and ground chicken or turkey.

In the deli section of your supermarket, you'll find smoked meat, smoked fish, or deli meats such as hot dogs, corned beef, and salami. These foods often contain both nitrites and nitrates, which have been known to cause stomach cancer. Remember that the fat and salt content of smoked foods is enough reason to limit your intake of them.

hot dogs Whether made from beef, chicken, veal, or pork, hot dogs are still one of the highest-fat meat choices. Even those labelled "lean" or "lite" are still loaded with fat, containing 9 to 12 grams of fat each, compared with 13 to 18 grams of fat for regular hot dogs. Hot dogs made with chicken or veal are not necessarily lower in fat because the manufacturers use the darker meat and often the chicken skin.

cold cuts Traditional packaged cold cuts are loaded with fat and sodium. Many are made from dark meat, skin, and high-cholesterol organ meats. Brands advertise "80% fat free," but that is fat by weight—such a product gets 77 percent of its calories from fat and has as much sodium in one serving as your daily requirement! Look for cold cuts that have 1 gram of fat or less per serving. You're better off with fresh sliced turkey from the deli counter. Avoid cold cuts containing nitrates, color, and additives.

fresh fish One of the healthiest forms of protein is fish. It is low in sodium and contains less saturated fat than red meat or chicken. A 4 ounce serving of a white fish has 146 calories, 2 grams of fat, and 54 milligrams of cholesterol; the same size serving of beef has 250 calories, 10 grams of fat, and 102 milligrams of cholesterol. Eat fish at least twice weekly to reap its benefits as a heart-healthy food. It contains omega-3 fatty acids, which can help lower blood cholesterol, triglyceride levels, and the risk of heart disease.

Lean fish include cod, halibut, snapper, sole, mussels, squid, and shellfish. Omega-3 fatty acids are found in fattier fish, such as salmon, trout, mackerel, albacore tuna, sea bass, and sardines.

Here are some tips on buying fish:

- Fish should be shiny and not have a fishy odor.
- If the fish is whole, the eyes should bulge and look clear. Cloudy eyes indicate that the fish is not fresh.
- Pre-wrapped fish you find in the supermarket is not always the freshest choice.
- If buying frozen fish, be sure it is clear of freezer burn and is vacuum sealed.
- If buying a whole fish, ask the fishmonger to "butterfly" it, removing the backbone and larger bones while still keeping the whole fish intact. You can just stuff and serve fish prepared in this way.
- If you get the fish home and it feels slimy or has a slight odor, rinse with cold water for a couple of minutes.
- Buy pieces of fish that are similar in size and weight so that their cooking times will be the same.
- For ultimate freshness, cook fresh fish the day you buy it.

canned fish Canned fish, such as salmon, tuna, sardines, and anchovies, contain similar nutrients to those found in fresh fish but usually have double the calories and 10 times the fat due to the oil in which they are packed. A better choice is canned fish packed in water.

shellfish Shellfish include shrimp, clams, mussels, lobster, crab, and scallops. Shellfish can contain higher amounts of cholesterol and more sodium than other fish, but they are still more nutritious than meat or poultry because the fat is unsaturated. A popular fish product called surimi is more commonly known as imitation crab. It is perfect for anyone with a shellfish allergy, since it is usually made from a mix of white fish, including Alaskan pollock, a deep-sea white fish.

legumes section

dried beans, peas, and lentils These are the only high-protein foods that contain fibre and can help lower cholesterol levels. Some of the more common varieties of beans are chick-peas, red and white kidney beans, navy beans, lima beans, soybeans, black beans, black-eyed beans, split peas, and green, red, and brown lentils.

Soy is the only plant-based food that is a complete protein and therefore is considered one of the healthiest foods available. It comes in various forms, as described next.

tofu Tofu or soybean curd is made from curdled soybean milk and is a main source of protein in Asian countries. A serving of 1/3 cup of tofu would replace a 3 ounce serving of meat, fish, or chicken and contain no saturated fat, no cholesterol, and fewer calories. Tofu comes in a variety of textures—firm, medium, or soft. The firm kind is wonderful as a substitute for meat or chicken and is great in stir-fries or casseroles. This kind of tofu is the highest in protein, calcium, and fat.

tempeh Tempeh is a chunky, fermented soybean cake containing rice or other grains. It can be marinated, grilled, or used in soups or casseroles.

miso A fermented soybean paste, miso can be used in soups, dips, sauces, and marinades.

ground soy Use this product in place of ground beef, in chili and spaghetti sauce, for example.

soy burgers, hot dogs, and salami These are soy alternatives to the regular meat products.

other soy foods A great variety of other soy products are available in stores today that are as delicious as they are versatile:

- Fresh soybeans (edamame)
- Dried soybeans or canned soybeans
- Dried roasted soybeans
- Soy milk
- Soy cheese, yogurt, and sour cream

canned, processed, and frozen foods section Fresh foods always have better texture and taste than canned or frozen foods, but at times it's difficult to have fresh foods on hand. Canned, frozen, or processed foods can contain excess fat, salt, and preservatives. Read the nutritional labels and look for products that, per serving, contain less than 15 grams of fat, less than 400 calories, and less than 800 milligrams of sodium. Surprisingly, frozen vegetables can be more nutritious than fresh ones, which may take days or even weeks to arrive on your shelves. When food is frozen, the nutrients are more potent since little time has elapsed between the picking and the freezing.

Canned food is a different matter. Compared with fresh food, it has fewer nutrients, often contains salt and other additives, which are included to preserve the food, and is inferior in texture and taste. Having certain canned foods on hand, however, makes cooking easier, more efficient, and less expensive. Acceptable canned products are canned tuna packed in water (not oil), canned soups (but avoid those that are cream based or contain excess sodium), tomato sauces that contain ripe tomatoes, legumes, and fruit packed in its own juice.

Prepackaged or canned soups are often primarily made of water, which is why they are low in calories. They are usually loaded with sodium and, if cream based, with cholesterol and fat. Stick to vegetable- and stock-based soups that are low in sodium.

snack aisle Avoid this area of the supermarket if you're hungry. Cookies, crackers, and potato and tortilla chips can contain hydrogenated vegetable fat or can be deep-fried and contain excess salt. Crackers can have as much fat as cookies.

Don't feel you can never go down this aisle, just choose snack foods ever so carefully and buy them in moderation. Here are some of the better choices:

- Popcorn (either home-popped or low-fat microwave varieties)
- Pretzels
- Baked tortilla chips
- Fruit bars and lower-fat granola bars
- Cookies such as animal crackers, digestive, or arrowroot, which don't have as much sugar and fat as other cookies
- Low-fat crackers such as Ry-Krisp, Melba toast, and rice cakes
- Salsa, or homemade dips instead of commercial dips

Beverages, candy, and cereals top the list of products that contain hidden sugar and empty calories. Nuts, on the other hand, are high in nutrition. Their greatest drawback is that they are loaded with calories and fat grams—approximately 200 calories and 20 grams of fat per ounce! Rather than having nuts as a snack, which allows you to overeat, toss a few into your recipes.

herbs and spices aisle In terms of healthier cooking, one of the best things you can do is reduce the amount of salt you use. Wean yourself off salt by experimenting with adding different herbs and spices to your cooking.

fresh versus dried herbs Fresh herbs are always a wonderful taste experience, but you must remember to add them only at the end of the cooking or as a garnish. If you add them during the cooking process, fresh herbs will lose most of their flavor and texture. For a more intense flavor, use dried herbs in cooking and fresh herbs as a garnish. When shopping for dried herbs, buy small amounts that you'll use in a short time; otherwise they lose their intensity over time. Freezing dried herbs, for up to one year, preserves their intensity.

There are so many herbs and spices you can use. The ones I always have on hand are dried basil, bay leaves, caraway seeds, cinnamon, cumin, curry, dill, oregano, paprika, chili powder, poppy seeds, rosemary, thyme, sesame seeds, and tarragon. Good fresh herbs to keep on hand are parsley, basil, dill, coriander, and chives.

sauces and condiments aisle Avoid sauces and dressings made with butter, cream, or excess oil. Read the product labels carefully. The order of ingredients tells you the primary ingredients in the product. Choose lower-fat versions of salad dressings and mayonnaise. Also beware of foods containing high levels of sodium, such as soy sauce and mustard.

mayonnaise Choose the lighter brands and use mayonnaise sparingly.

ketchup Ketchup is high in sodium and sugar, so it use sparingly.

peanut butter Purchase peanut butter that is made from peanuts only. The other types often contain icing sugar and are hydrogenated, which means this naturally wonderful food becomes saturated. If the oil rises to the top, just mix firmly until blended.

salad dressings A single serving of regular Caesar salad (the kind on many restaurant menus) can contain up to 600 calories and 35 grams of fat. Just 2 tablespoons of regular bottled salad dressing contain approximately 120 calories and 12 grams of fat! Use lower-fat varieties.

salsa Chopped tomatoes, onions, lemon, herbs, and hot peppers are combined in this low-fat condiment. It is great with baked tortilla chips, as a topping for potatoes or burgers, and even as a salad dressing.

storing your groceries

Here are some tips on storing your healthy food once you get it home. Of course, before you use a product, always check the product expiration date, which refers to the date by which it's best to use the product for maximum freshness. (The meaning of the various product dates is discussed in "The Refrigerator" on page 22.)

the pantry Keep a supply of basic ingredients, as well as some canned, jarred, or bottled foods, in your pantry, and you'll be able to whip up a meal in no time.

flour White flour can be kept unopened in the pantry for up to one year, and once opened for up to eight months. Whole wheat flour is more delicate and can be stored for only for one month in the pantry but for up to eight months if refrigerated.

sugar Store sugar in the pantry. It never spoils. Have available granulated, brown, and icing sugar.

baking powder and baking soda Both can be kept in the pantry unopened for up to eight months, and once opened for between three and six months.

baking ingredients These include vanilla or almond extract; semi-sweet, white, or other flavored chocolate chips; unsweetened cocoa; cornstarch; cookie crumbs; and unflavored gelatin.

canned goods Most canned foods can be kept for up to five years in the pantry, but, once opened, canned goods must be kept in the refrigerator and only for up to five days. However, if canned foods are frozen in airtight containers, they can be kept for six months.

Here are some basic canned ingredients to have handy.

- Variety of beans
- Whole or diced tomatoes
- Corn niblets
- Tomato paste
- Tuna packed in water
- Water chestnuts
- Baby corn
- Mandarin oranges
- Sliced olives in water
- Canola vegetable spray
- Light coconut milk
- Evaporated milk
- Tomato paste
- Anchovies

vegetable oils Keep unopened oil in the pantry for up to eight months; once opened, store oil in a dark, cool place for up to six months. Oils do not need to be refrigerated.

vinegars Balsamic, rice wine, cider, and red wine vinegars can be kept in the pantry for over a year unopened. Once opened, these vinegars can be stored for three to six months if refrigerated.

jams and jellies If unopened, jams and jellies can be stored for one year in the pantry; once opened, refrigerate them for up to six months.

peanut butter Buy natural, non-hydrogenated peanut butter that contains no added sugar. Store it unopened in the pantry for up to one year and, once opened, in the refrigerator for up to three months.

tomato-based pasta sauces These can be kept unopened for a year and refrigerated for three weeks once open.

condiments These include lower-fat salad dressings, light mayonnaise, ketchup, sweet chili sauce, barbeque sauce, salsa, hot sauce, plum sauce, Dijon mustard, and roasted red peppers packed in water. Most condiments, if unopened, can be kept in the pantry for a year or more. Once opened, condiments can be refrigerated for six months or longer.

pasta and rice Unopened, these grains can be kept in the pantry for up to two years; once opened, use them within one year. Other grains, such as quinoa, millet, spelt, or bulgur, are more delicate. Store these grains frozen for up to one year.

cereal Keep unopened cereal in the pantry for up to one year; once opened, use cereal within six months.

coffee Unopened packaged coffee will keep for up to two years; use coffee within a month once the package has been opened. Keep coffee tightly covered. You can freeze coffee to lengthen its shelf life.

breads and grains These include the following:

- Sliced whole wheat bread (keep extra loaves in the freezer)
- Flavored tortillas, pitas, and sandwich buns, preferably whole wheat products (keep extras in the freezer)
- Cold cereals containing extra fibre, dried fruits, and little sugar
- Hot cereals such as Cream of Wheat or oatmeal
- Lower-fat granola and Grape Nuts cereal for baking

the refrigerator Keep your refrigerator stocked with a reasonable supply of dairy products, meat and poultry, and fruits and vegetables. Product dates are usually displayed on most food items. Always check product dates. Here's what they mean:

- The **best before date** refers to the last day an item should be sold.
- The **expiration date** is the last day that the item should be sold or eaten.
- The **freshness date** is stamped on by the manufacturer to indicate how long freshness is guaranteed.
- The **pack date** is the date the product was packaged or processed by the manufacturer. This date does not indicate for how long the food will remain good.

cheese The hard cheeses keep the longest and the unripened cheeses have the shortest shelf life.

butter and margarine Butter can be kept in the refrigerator for up to three months and in the freezer for up to nine months. Margarine, preferably non-hydrogenated, soft tub margarine, can be kept slightly longer.

eggs It's best to keep eggs in the original container instead of in the egg container on the refrigerator door. Use eggs within three to five weeks. Leftover egg whites or yolks can be kept for up to five days. Do not leave eggs out of the refrigerator for longer than two hours at room temperature.

Hard-cooked eggs can be stored—in the shell—for a maximum of 10 days in the refrigerator. You can freeze raw whole eggs (not in their shell), egg whites, or just the yolks. The best way to freeze whole eggs is to beat them first and then put them in a container with a tight lid. If you are freezing only the yolks, beat them first and add 1/4 teaspoon of salt or 1-1/2 teaspoons of sugar for every four egg yolks.

meat Raw meat can be kept in the coldest part of the refrigerator for up to two or three days.

poultry Poultry keeps only one to two days, and fish or seafood for two days. Cooked meat can be kept for up to four days or, if wrapped properly, in the freezer for up to four months. Cold cuts can be kept for up to five days in the refrigerator and in the freezer for up to two months. Hot dogs can be kept for up to a week and frozen for two months or longer.

vegetables and fruits Vegetables are great for salads, side dishes, snacks, and cooking, particularly in stir-fries. Some common ones to have around are asparagus, broccoli, cauliflower, carrots, celery, cucumbers, green beans, green onions, lettuce, mushrooms, onions, sweet peppers, potatoes, sweet potatoes, and tomatoes.

Each vegetable has different storage requirements, but most should be stored in the vegetable crisper and used within five to seven days. Don't wash vegetables before storing them. If you plan to store them in a plastic bag, make some holes in it first so that the vegetables can "breathe." Vegetables such as onions, potatoes, garlic, gingerroot, and squash don't need to be refrigerated until cut. I keep my tomatoes on the counter to ripen and refrigerate them only when ripe.

Wash all fruits and vegetables under running tap water just before eating them or preparing them for cooking. Washing with soap isn't necessary. If you want to remove dirt or wax more thoroughly, buy a fruit and vegetable wash, which works very well. For convenience, you can buy greens that have been pre-washed and dried. They are either labelled "pre-washed" or "triple-washed."

Always have fruits—oranges, grapefruit, lemons, pears, peaches, melons, berries, and so on—available for quick snacks.

the global pantry I like to think of my pantry as the "global" pantry—a cupboard in which I can always find an ingredient from world cuisines. Keeping a supply of some staple ingredients used in these cuisines will allow you to prepare a variety of interesting dishes. You should be able to find these ingredients in most supermarkets.

asian pantry The more common ingredients are long-grain rice, sushi rice, soy sauce, sesame oil, rice wine vinegar, hoisin sauce, oyster sauce, fish sauce, plum sauce, hot chili sauce, black bean sauce, rice noodles, nori (seaweed), wasabi (Japanese horseradish), canned baby corn, canned water chestnuts, canned mandarin oranges, gingerroot, garlic, and sesame seeds.

mediterranean pantry A Mediterranean pantry should be stocked with canned tomatoes, tomato paste, black and green olives, roasted red peppers packed in water, anchovies, Dijon mustard, seasoned bread crumbs, cornmeal, Arborio rice, sun-dried tomatoes, basil, oregano, bay leaves, a variety of canned beans, olive oil, and balsamic vinegar.

mexican or latin american pantry Having on hand a variety of canned beans, as well as jalapeño peppers, baked tortilla chips, avocado, salsa, light sour cream, flour tortillas, rice, and lower-fat cheeses, will enable you to make some interesting and easy dishes.

middle eastern pantry Healthy and interesting dishes are easy to make if you have available chick-peas, tahini (sesame paste), bulgur, couscous, brown rice, pitas, cumin, and fresh coriander.

north american pantry Basic ingredients include different kinds of pasta, lower-fat cheeses, pasta sauce, lean meats, and condiments such as mustard, ketchup, sweet chili sauce, light mayonnaise, and low-fat sour cream.

vegetarian pantry I love to prepare vegetarian meals occasionally for my family. You don't have to be a vegetarian to enjoy a meatless meal. Having a variety of grains, vegetables, sauces, and soy products in your pantry allows you to produce excellent vegetarian meals. Some useful ingredients for vegetarian cooking include firm and soft tofu; ground soy to substitute for ground meat; soy products, such as soy bacon, hot dogs, hamburgers, and pepperoni slices; and soy milk, yogurt, cheese, sour cream, and cream cheese to substitute for dairy products.

the freezer The standing joke I have with friends, students, and clients is about the number of freezers I have in my home. I always say that another freezer is more useful to me than a fur coat or diamonds! The way to be organized in my home is to have available in bulk many of the following foods, which can be frozen.

nuts, dried fruits, and grains I often purchase a variety of nuts, dried fruits, and grains at a large bulk food warehouse. Freezing prevents nuts and grains from becoming rancid or stale. Dried fruits, such as cranberries, raisins, pitted dates, and apricots, thaw quickly or can be placed in the microwave for 30 seconds to make them easier to chop. The grains I freeze are those that I can't find easily in the supermarket, such as quinoa, millet, wheatberries, and bulgur. I like to have on hand pecans, cashews, almonds, pine nuts, peanuts, and macadamias.

sun-dried tomatoes I always keep a large bag of these in the freezer. To rehydrate them, pour boiling water over the amount needed and let stand for about 15 minutes. Avoid buying jarred sun-dried tomatoes packed in oil. They contain too many calories and fat from the excess oil.

meat Have some meat available in your freezer for weekday meals. Learn how to defrost properly in the microwave, or place the frozen meat in the refrigerator to thaw slowly. Have meat vacuum sealed if possible to prevent deterioration and freezer burn. Your supermarket, butcher, or wholesaler should provide this service. I package meat in 1 pound quantities. Keep some of the following meats in your freezer:

- Boneless single chicken breasts and thighs, chicken legs and breasts with bones, and whole chickens
- Lean ground beef, chicken, pork, or turkey
- Lean steaks including rib-eye, tenderloin, flank, and sirloin
- Beef, veal, or pork tenderloins
- Roasts and stewing beef

vegetables and fruits I always prefer to cook with fresh vegetables, but having a selection of vegetables you enjoy on hand in the freezer can allow you make that casserole or stir-fry when you walk in the door. These vegetables were picked and frozen within a short time period. Vegetables that are sold fresh may be picked, packaged, and shipped long distances, and this sometimes lengthy process allows for nutrient loss.

Keep a selection of fruits frozen without sugar in the freezer for baking purposes. Strawberries, raspberries, blueberries, and peaches are great selections. Unless the recipe recommends using fruit when it is still frozen (for example, blueberries) always defrost and drain frozen fruits before using them to get rid of excess water.

dairy products Freeze butter and blocks of cheese such as mozzarella, Cheddar, Swiss, and Parmesan for cooking purposes only. To use frozen cheese, defrost slightly and then grate.

packing for the freezer Packaging foods properly before freezing them can preserve the quality of your food until you're ready to use it. We've all seen freezer burn and ice crystals on food that we packaged improperly. Here are four ways to help preserve the freshness in your frozen food:

1. Packaging must be moisture- and vapor-proof to preserve the nutritional value of foods and prevent their drying out. Squeeze the air out of bags before freezing.
2. Rigid containers and plastic bags need airtight seals. Seal the edges of containers with freezer tape to ensure freshness. Wrapped foods are best stored in extra heavy aluminum foil, freezer plastic, or polyethylene-lined paper.
3. Label all containers and bags with the name of the food and the date.
4. To freeze hot foods, divide them into useable portions and freeze them with enough space around the containers to permit cooled air to circulate around them. This will prevent the temperature in the freezer from rising, thus affecting other foods.

freezer storage times Here are some guidelines for storing frozen foods:

Storage Time for Frozen Foods

Beef and pork roasts and steaks	6 months to 1 year
Ground beef	3 to 4 months
Lamb	6 to 9 months
Chicken parts	9 months
Whole chicken or turkey	1 year
Fish: fattier fish	3 months
leaner fish	3 to 6 months
Shrimp: in shell	6 to 12 months
peeled	3 to 4 months
Fruit juice concentrates	1 year
Ice cream, frozen yogurt, etc.	1 month
Cooked meat dishes	2 to 3 months
Vegetables and fruits	8 months to 1 year

cookware and kitchen equipment

When buying and using cookware, keep these four guidelines in mind:

1. Purchase a set of good quality nonstick frying pans, saucepans, and baking pans. They allow you to cook using only cooking spray or a minimal amount of oil, water, or stock. Some of the better-known brand name nonstick coatings are Teflon 2 and Silverstone, and some of the improved coatings are T-Fal and Silverstone Extra. These coatings are inert carbon-fluorine polymers, so nothing sticks to them and they don't react to acids in foods.

2. Choose heavier pans because they last a long time, conduct and retain the heat better than lighter pans, and do not have hot spots. Some of the better brands of nonstick cookware include All-Clad, Lagostina, Cuisinart, Excalibur, and Calphalon, to name a few. Use regular (not nonstick) cookware for any type of cooking not requiring sautéing.

3. To avoid scratching your nonstick cookware, don't use an abrasive cleaner or metal utensils. Once the pans have been scratched, they don't work as effectively and food cooked in them may not be healthy for you (see "Cookware Safety," below). Buy nonstick utensils that are sturdy, useful, and well designed.

4. If you want to give food a grilled appearance, use a nonstick grill pan or an electric grill. The advantage of using these is that you won't have to step outside in the winter to do the barbecuing, and food cooked in them is delicious and low in fat.

cookware safety Materials from your cookware can leach into your foods, especially if the cookware is scratched. Keep these important safety facts in mind:

- Stainless steel is safe for cooking and storing food and is the most popular type of cookware. Often it is coated with a nonstick coating.
- The connection between aluminum cookware and Alzheimer's disease is still unproven. Adults can consume at least 50 milligrams of aluminum daily without harm. You would absorb daily only 1 to 2 milligrams of the aluminum from aluminum cookware you used regularly.
- Copper cookware is coated with another metal to prevent the copper from coming in contact with the food. Do not use copper pots that do not have this coating.
- Nonstick coatings are chemically inert, which means that any material they release passes through the body without breaking down or being absorbed.
- Certain glazes used on ceramics, especially those designed to be fired at low temperatures, may release lead and cadmium into food or liquids placed in them.

cooking utenstils and equipment

knives For everyday cooking you will need a good quality chopping knife, a serrated knife, and a paring knife. So many people hate the chopping required to prepare meals because their knives are of poor quality or are not sharp. Go to a kitchen specialty store where the staff can show you the best knife for your price range and the size of your hand. Try the knife to ensure that it fits your hand comfortably.

electrical equipment Let these small appliances do some of the work for you:

- Food processor—select one with a large capacity bowl if you cook in larger quantities
- Hand beater
- Electric mixer
- Rice cooker if you enjoy lots of rice-based meals—choose one with a warming feature and a lockable lid
- Toaster oven (for roasting peppers, broiling, reheating small quantities)
- Slow cooker

basic equipment A well-equipped kitchen has all of the following:

- Set of good quality nonstick pots and pans
- Nonstick wok
- Baking dishes—8-inch, 9-inch, 13- × 9-inch
- Nonstick baking sheets
- Springform pans
- Ovenproof casserole dishes
- Roasting pan
- Loaf pans
- Measuring utensils for dry and wet ingredients
- Plastic and metal whisks
- Heat-resistant spatulas
- Wooden spoons
- Salad spinner
- Colander
- Mixing bowls of various sizes
- Cutting boards—a wooden one and a plastic, dishwasher-safe one
- Good quality zester
- Vegetable peeler

- Microwave-safe dishes and containers
- Freezer bags and containers
- Timer
- Weigh scale
- Oven thermometer

cooking methods

Various cooking methods for lower-fat cooking are described below. Take note that deep-frying is no longer in my cooking vocabulary since food cooked this way becomes saturated in oil, fat, and excess calories. Here's a comparison of the results from using different cooking methods: four fried chicken fingers can contain 200 calories and 11 grams of fat; when baked, they contain approximately 100 calories and 1 gram of fat! So examine the cooking methods you've been using and make some healthy changes.

cooking in liquid

steaming This method involves cooking food over boiling water—holding the food above the water to cook in the steam—and is one of the best methods for retaining nutrients. Steamed vegetables lose 50 percent fewer nutrients than boiled vegetables.

boiling To preserve the nutrients in foods, boil them in as little water as possible and add them when the water is boiling. Save the nutrient-rich water to use in soups.

poaching With this method, food is simmered in a liquid that is kept just below the boiling point. Eggs and fish are commonly poached.

stewing Stewing is a method used to cook tougher cuts of meat at a slow, gentle simmer to make them tender. This is a great way to cook inexpensive cuts of meat.

high-heat cooking
Even though barbecuing, grilling, sautéing, and broiling are low-fat forms of cooking, some health hazards result if meat gets crispy or charred. When smoke is created by burning fat, cancer-causing chemicals called polycyclic aromatic hydrocarbons (PAHs) are formed. When you plan to use these cooking methods, always choose leaner cuts of meat, fish, or chicken to reduce your chances of exposure to these carcinogens.

grilling or barbecuing This popular form of cooking is inherently low in fat and calories. I use either a barbecue or a nonstick grill pan that can be placed on the stove. Today, virtually every food is being put on the grill. To protect yourself from carcinogens, choose the leanest meats, fish, and poultry; barbecue slowly; raise the grill as far from the coals as possible; and don't let your food touch the flames or catch fire.

broiling When broiled, food is cooked at 500°F for a short time. Sweet peppers are charred in this manner (the skin is later removed, not eaten), and bread can be toasted. Toppings are browned for a few minutes under the broiler.

frying and sautéing Frying uses excess oil, which translates into foods that are higher in fat and calories. For lower-fat cooking, this method is not appropriate.

Sautéing requires a small amount of oil to cook foods. Use a nonstick frying pan and some cooking spray when you sauté vegetables, meat, or fish. This method reduces the calories and fat considerably.

cooking in the oven

baking and roasting These are common methods of cooking meats, fish, and some vegetables. To retain moisture, bake or roast at a higher temperature, between 375°F and 425°F, for a shorter period of time. Be sure to place a rack on the bottom of the roasting pan to prevent food from sitting in the released fat. Pouring about 1/2 cup of stock or water into the bottom of the pan will prevent the pan from burning and provide an instant gravy for meats and chicken. Keep in mind that fat drips into the liquid.

microwaving This is the best cooking method to preserve nutrients. I like to microwave vegetables and fish. A microwave is also great for heating and defrosting. Use the microwave to partially cook foods before you barbecue them. Place the thickest part of the food toward the outside of the plate; when the food is almost done, let it sit for a few minutes to finish cooking.

The basic problem with this method is cooking food for too long. The key is to microwave on High for a short time. To be safe, microwave for less time than you think necessary, and then microwave for additional short periods as needed.

nutrient loss No matter how you cook food, some nutrient loss will result. The amount of nutrients lost will depend on the freshness of the food, how it has been handled and stored before you obtained it, how long you cook it for, and the temperature at which it is cooked. Precut produce is convenient but contains lower levels of nutrients.

Here are some ways to minimize nutrient loss:

- Cook the food for the shortest time possible. Microwaving, stir-frying, and steaming are the best methods. Baking or roasting at high temperatures retains the moisture content of the food but lessens the nutrient value.
- Cook vegetables whole and unpeeled, or eat them raw. Most vegetables are more nutritious when eaten raw, except for carrots, which are more nutritious when cooked.
- Never soak fruits or vegetables in water.
- Boil vegetables in as little water as possible.

light cooking Once you've made the commitment to change your way of eating, some simple but important practices will make the transition successful. It may take some time until you do them without thinking, but once you do, you'll never return to your old habits.

light cooking with dairy Milk containing either 1 percent or 2 percent MF is excellent for cooking and baking. I don't recommend using milk with a lower MF content because it is watery and will not give your food the desired texture.

Yogurt that contains 1 percent or 2 percent MF is excellent for cooking and baking. Avoid the higher-fat Balkan-style yogurts, which contain 4 percent MF or more. When adding yogurt to sauces, be sure that the sauce is not too hot or the yogurt will curdle.

Sour cream containing anywhere from 1 percent to 5 percent MF is an excellent substitute for regular sour cream, which has 14 percent MF. Use low-fat sour cream for cooking or baking. As with yogurt, to prevent curdling add sour cream slowly to sauces that are not too hot.

If you want to cook with higher-fat cheese, such as Brie, Camembert, Parmesan, Asiago, blue, or Swiss, and no lower-fat substitutes are available, then keep the quantity to no more than 1 ounce per person. Cook dishes that contain a lot of cheese only occasionally.

Hard cheeses, such as Cheddar, Swiss, mozzarella, and Parmesan, usually contain between 28 percent and 35 percent MF. I like to cook with cheeses that contain between 9 percent and 15 percent MF, which is a saving of at least 50 percent in calories and fat. Some hard cheeses contain as little as 4 percent MF, but I think they lack flavor and texture. They melt poorly and give your foods a "plastic" taste.

Ricotta cheese, now a staple in my home for cooking and baking, traditionally contains 10 percent MF, but an excellent 5 percent MF version is available. I would not recommend using ricotta that contains less fat because the cheese will be too dry. Be sure to find a smooth, creamy ricotta cheese that will give your cooking the best texture. You can add a couple of tablespoons of milk, yogurt, or sour cream to overly firm ricotta to make it smoother.

Goat and feta cheeses are great for cooking because of their distinct flavors and the fact that you need very little of them to achieve an intense taste. These cheeses are lower in fat than regular hard and soft cheeses. Goat and feta cheeses usually contain 15 percent MF, and today you can find delicious feta cheeses that contain as little as 10 percent MF.

removing fat from meats Trim all visible fat from beef, chicken, pork, and other meats before cooking them. With chicken, I leave the skin on all cuts except when a recipe calls for skinless breasts. The skin preserves the moisture and flavor in the chicken. The fat does not penetrate the meat, and you can season the meat under the skin. The trick is to remove the skin before eating the chicken. Cooking chicken with the skin on will add only 1 gram of fat to your dish, and the food will be that much more flavorful.

removing fat from soups and stocks Removing and discarding fat from soups is easy if you chill the soup until the fat solidifies on top. If a recipe calls for cream, substitute milk or evaporated milk. To thicken soups without using cream, butter, egg yolks, or a butter-and-flour mixture (a roux), use cooked vegetables that are already puréed or purée the soup. Always have a variety of stocks on hand to cook with. They add flavor and replace the cream, milk, butter, and oil in many recipes. You can use homemade stock, or you can buy stocks canned, in bouillon cubes, powdered, as concentrates, or in sealed packs. If using powdered stock, add 1 teaspoon to 1 cup of boiling water. I purchase stocks that contain no preservatives or MSG.

using high-fat ingredients in moderation You don't have to omit high-fat ingredients, such as nuts, chocolate, and coconut, from your cooking and baking. Simply use them in moderation to highlight a recipe.

Use no more than 2 ounces or 1/4 cup of nuts in your cooking or baking. This amount contains 400 calories and 40 grams of fat. Toasting your nuts gives them a better flavor. A great low-fat substitute is Grape Nuts cereal, low-fat granola, or a combination of both.

Use no more than 1/3 cup chocolate chips or a 3 ounce square in a recipe. Use cocoa as a substitute for chocolate and just as a highlight. Cocoa has all the chocolate flavor without the cocoa butter. Instead of 1 ounce of semi-sweet chocolate in a recipe, use 1-1/2 tablespoons of cocoa plus 2 tablespoons of sugar and 2 teaspoons of butter, margarine, or vegetable oil. Heat the mixture until the sugar melts.

Coconut adds great taste and texture to cooking and baking, but keep the amount of coconut low since it contains saturated fat. Toasting the coconut gives it a better flavor.

reducing the fat in desserts You can lessen the fat by as much as 50 percent in baked goods. The trick is to maintain the moisture that fat adds to cakes and other baking. For example, the amount of oil, butter, or margarine in a recipe can be reduced to one-half or one-third of that called for by substituting fruit or vegetables—such as puréed bananas, cooked dates or prunes, applesauce, grated carrots or zucchini—for the rest of the fat. I also like to use lower-fat yogurt, sour cream, or butter-milk to replace some of the fat.

Frostings or decorations for cakes are usually made with butter, lard, cream, or vegetable short-ening. Lower-fat substitutions include light cream cheese or ricotta cheese. Or, use icing sugar and a small amount of a liquid, such as fruit juice, water, or even liqueurs, to form a glaze.

Beaten egg whites add volume and tenderness to cakes and desserts without the fat. I use them in cakes, cheesecakes, and mousse recipes in which whipping cream would traditionally be used.

using puréed or grated vegetables to replace fat Use puréed or grated vegetables as wonderful replacements for the fat in all kinds of dishes:

- Cooked vegetables can be used to thicken puréed soups.
- Puréed peas can be substituted for avocado in guacamole.
- Puréed or grated sweet potatoes, carrots, or zucchini are great to use in cakes or muffins.
- Vegetables can replace some of the cheese and meat sauce in lasagnas and pizzas.

making lower-fat sauces To make a sauce without using cream or butter, mix equal amounts of milk and any kind of stock. For every 1 cup of liquid, add 1 tablespoon of flour or 2 teaspoons of corn-starch and mix until smooth. Heat for approximately 3 minutes, stirring constantly, until the sauce is slightly thickened. To add variety, use such ingredients as sautéed mushrooms, shrimp, or cheese. For a thicker sauce, substitute a lower-fat evaporated milk for the milk.

making lower-fat salad dressings Don't feel you have to omit salad dressings or resort to using only lemon juice or vinegar. Use dressings in moderation and try not to add more than 2 tablespoons to your salad. Using a low-fat dressing is also good, but remember still to use smaller amounts.

The better choice for salad dressing is homemade, for two reasons: homemade dressing tastes better, and it's usually made with less fat than store-bought dressings. I often use orange juice con-centrate, flavored vinegars, a little water, and more flavorful oils, such as sesame or olive oil, so that I can reduce the amount of regular oil.

substituting ingredients Using lower-fat ingredients to replace high-fat foods will help decrease the calories, fat, cholesterol, and sodium in your meals. With the right substitutions, you should have an excellent, rich dish with great taste and texture. Ingredient substitution is the basis for all my recipes.

Ingredient	Lower-Fat Substitution
Whole milk	Milk, 2% MF or less
Heavy cream	Evaporated milk, 2% MF
Sour cream	Sour cream, 5% MF or less; lower-fat yogurt
Mayonnaise	Lower-fat mayonnaise, yogurt, or sour cream
Butter	Non-hydrogenated margarine; canola oil; olive oil
1 whole egg	2 egg whites; an egg substitute
Cream cheese	Light cream cheese; ricotta cheese; lower-fat cottage cheese
Chocolate	Cocoa
Ice cream	Frozen sorbet; frozen yogurt
Salad dressings	Low-fat homemade; low-fat store-bought
Pesto sauce	Low-fat recipe: equal amounts pesto and light cream cheese, yogurt, sour cream, or stock
Tortilla chips	Baked tortilla chips
Nuts (for cooking and baking)	Grape Nuts cereal; lower-fat granola; water chestnuts
Salt	Herbs or non-sodium seasoning
Ground meat	Ground chicken, ground turkey, ground soy

reducing the sugar in desserts In any recipe, you can reduce the sugar by at least 25 percent without changing the texture or flavor significantly. Try adding a pinch of spice, such as cinnamon, nutmeg, allspice, or vanilla or almond extract to heighten the flavor.

a month of menus

Here is a one-month weekday wonders menu plan. You can use it to help you plan meals for a month, a week, or even just a couple of days. The main course often is enough nutritionally to stand on its own, but feel free to add a salad, soup, or side dish of your choice. A light dessert is always welcome!

You'll find a shopping list and storage tips as well. The "Make Ahead" sections of the recipes tell you what you can prepare in advance.

week 1 monday

Hoisin Chicken with Couscous (page 177), Black Bean Soup (page 55)
The baked chicken can be frozen in portions for up to 3 months. The soup can be frozen for up to 3 months; defrost it in the microwave or overnight in the refrigerator.

tuesday

Creamy Seafood and Dill Casserole over Rice (page 114)
This casserole can be frozen for up to 6 weeks.

wednesday

Spaghetti with Creamy Tomato Meat Sauce and Cheese Topping (page 154)
Freeze in individual portions for up to 3 months.

thursday

Greek-Style Chicken (page 176), Sliced Tomato Stacks (page 102)
The chicken can be frozen for up to 6 weeks. The tomatoes can be refrigerated for up to 2 days.

friday

Pesto- and Feta-Crusted Rack of Lamb (page 165), Yukon Gold and Sweet Potato Mash (page 108)
The cooked lamb can be frozen for up to 6 weeks. The potato mash can be refrigerated for up to 3 days or frozen for up to 1 month.

groceries

meats/fish

2-1/2 lb boneless chicken breasts
12 oz shrimp

1-1/2 lb rack of lamb
12 oz scallops

8 oz lean ground beef

dairy products

Parmesan cheese
light ricotta cheese
low-fat sour cream

mozzarella cheese
light cream cheese

feta cheese
goat cheese

fresh produce

onions
sweet red pepper
garlic, gingerroot

carrots
plum and field tomatoes
sweet potatoes

green onions
parsley, dill, coriander
Yukon Gold potatoes

pantry foods

2 cans (12 oz) 2% evaporated milk
Asian chili sauce
hoisin sauce
tomato pasta sauce
jasmine or basmati rice
soy sauce
sun-dried tomatoes
liquid honey
sesame seeds

hot pepper sauce
sugar
couscous
spaghetti
bread crumbs
ketchup
pine nuts
olive oil
flour

dried oregano, basil, cumin
cornstarch
1 can (19 oz) black beans
canned sliced black olives
Dijon mustard
various stocks
salt and pepper
vegetable oil

frozen/refrigerated foods

pesto

orange juice concentrate

week 2   monday

Salmon with Maple Hoisin Sauce (page 197), Asian-Flavored Swiss Chard (page 103)
The fish can be frozen with sauce for up to 2 weeks. Cooked Swiss chard can be refrigerated for up to 3 days but is best cooked just before serving.

tuesday

Chicken with Avocado Tomato Salsa (page 172), Tomato and Onion Salad with Feta Cheese
  Dressing (page 81)
The chicken can be refrigerated for up to 3 days. The salad can be refrigerated for up to 2 days. The
dressing can be made in advance and refrigerated for up to 2 days.

wednesday

Flank Steak in Black Bean Sauce with Bok Choy (page 162), Tomato Potato Salad (page 84)
The cooked steak in sauce can be frozen for up to 6 weeks. The salad can be refrigerated for up to
2 days.

thursday

Southwest Tortilla Bake (page 214), Vegetable Crouton Salad (page 78)
The tortilla dish, unbaked, can be frozen for up to 2 months. Leftovers can be frozen for up to
1 month. The salad is best the day it is prepared.

friday

Hoisin Veal Chops (page 158), Miso Soup with Chow Mein Noodles, Chicken, and Tofu (use shrimp
  instead of chicken if desired) (page 60)
The baked veal chops can be frozen with sauce for up to 2 months. The soup can be frozen for up to
2 months.

groceries   ### meats/fish

1 lb salmon fillets	1-1/2 lb flank steak
4-1/2 lb boneless chicken breasts	1 lb bone-in veal chops

dairy products

feta cheese	light sour cream	light mayonnaise
mozzarella cheese	light ricotta cheese	light cream cheese

fresh produce

1 lb Swiss chard	1 bunch bok choy	3 lb plum tomatoes
English cucumber	avocado	lemons or limes
2 large field tomatoes	sweet onions	sweet red, yellow, or green peppers
green onions	12 small red potatoes	1/4 lb firm tofu
garlic, gingerroot	parsley, coriander, basil	onions

pantry foods

maple syrup	hoisin sauce	Dijon mustard
balsamic vinegar	sesame oil	soy sauce (low sodium)
rice wine vinegar	sliced black olives	dried oregano, basil, cumin
1 can (8 oz) corn niblets	chicken, beef, vegetable stock	natural peanut butter
brown sugar	ketchup	black bean sauce
2 cans (19 oz) red kidney beans	medium salsa	cornstarch
1 sheet nori	liquid honey	vegetable oil
hot Asian chili sauce	olive oil	sugar
hot sauce	bread crumbs	4 cans hearts of palm
pepper	flour	

frozen/refrigerated foods

flavored tortillas	orange juice concentrate	yellow miso paste
fresh chow mein noodles		

week 3 ## monday

Veggie Burgers (page 210), Spinach and Mango Salad with Black Bean Dressing (page 83)
The burgers can be sautéed and frozen for up to 2 months. The salad can be refrigerated for 1 day without the dressing.

tuesday

Chicken and Bean Mediterranean Chili (page 118)
The chili can be frozen for up to 2 months or refrigerated for up to 3 days.

wednesday

Mussels with Creamy Tomato Sauce (page 202), Vegetable Crouton Salad (page 78)
The mussels can be refrigerated for up to 1 day. The salad is best when served the same day it is made but can be refrigerated without the dressing for up to 1 day.

thursday

Hoisin Garlic Burgers (page 127), Sweet Potato Fries with Cinnamon and Maple Syrup (page 107)
The burgers can be prepared and frozen as patties for up to 6 months. Once cooked, they can be frozen for up to 2 months. The potato fries can be refrigerated for up to 2 days.

friday

Sesame-Crusted Salmon with Asian Sauce (page 198), Roasted Corn Black Bean Salad (page 88)
The salmon can be frozen for up to 2 weeks. Corn salad can be refrigerated for up to 2 days.

groceries

meats/fish

2 lb mussels	12 oz boneless chicken breast	1 lb lean ground beef
1-1/2 lb salmon fillets		

fresh produce

onions	garlic, gingerroot	1 lb plum tomatoes
English cucumber	sweet red and green peppers	1/2 lb mushrooms
carrots	basil, parsley, coriander	lemons
2 large sweet potatoes	oyster mushrooms	1 large mango
2 cans (8 oz each) corn niblets	green onions	baby spinach
lettuce	sweet onions	

dairy products

feta cheese	light Cheddar cheese	light sour cream

pantry foods

cornstarch	liquid honey	black bean sauce
2% evaporated milk	various stocks	dried basil
French or Italian bread	canned sliced black olives	Dijon mustard
tomato pasta sauce	canned chick-peas	bread crumbs
soy sauce (low sodium)	hoisin sauce	sesame oil
maple syrup	sesame seeds	hot sauce
canned black beans	vegetable oil	rice wine vinegar
olive oil	balsamic vinegar	sugar
pepper	dried oregano, chili powder, basil, cinnamon, ginger, nutmeg	

frozen/refrigerated foods

orange juice concentrate   eggs

week 4   monday

Basil Meatloaf with Yukon Gold Potato Topping (page 123)
Baked or unbaked, the meatloaf can be frozen for up to 1 month.

tuesday

Grilled Tuna with Greek Tomato Salsa (page 193)
This dish can be refrigerated for up to 1 day or frozen for up to 2 weeks.

wednesday

Chinese Beef with Crisp Vegetables (page 136), Udon Noodle Soup with Chicken and Shrimp (page 59)
The stir-fry can be frozen for up to 1 month.

thursday

Chicken Teriaki over Rotini (page 150)
This dish can be refrigerated for up to 1 day. The sauce can be frozen for up to 2 months.

friday

Stuffed Zucchini (page 209), Chick-Pea Salad with Tahini Dressing (page 89)
The stuffing can be refrigerated for up to 3 days. The baked zucchini and the salad can be
refrigerated for up to 2 days.

groceries

meats/fish

12 oz lean ground beef	1-1/2 lb tuna	12 oz boneless grilling steak
1 lb boneless chicken breasts	4 oz raw shrimp	

fresh produce

1 lb Yukon Gold potatoes	sweet onions	garlic, gingerroot
plum tomatoes	lemons	basil or parsley, coriander
broccoli	snow peas	carrots
celery	1 cup bean sprouts	green onions
2 large zucchini	bok choy	onions
sweet green, red, and yellow peppers		

dairy products

smooth 5% ricotta cheese	light sour cream	6 oz fresh udon noodles
Parmesan cheese	light cream cheese	light feta cheese

pantry foods

salt	sesame seeds	canned sliced black olives
dried basil, oregano, cumin	barbeque sauce	bread crumbs
various stocks	brown sugar	soy sauce (low sodium)
rice wine vinegar	sesame oil	cornstarch
1 can (19 oz) chick-peas	vegetable oil	olive oil
tahini (sesame seed paste)	pine nuts	salt and pepper
rotini	toasted cashews	light mayonnaise

frozen/refrigerated foods

eggs	sun-dried tomatoes

meat

chicken and turkey

fish and seafood

super quick

super quick recipes

recipes ready in 20 minutes or less

soups

vegetarian main dishes

desserts

recipes

soups

yukon gold and sweet potato soup

PREP: About 15 mins.
COOK: About 25 mins.

MAKES 6 SERVINGS

MAKE AHEAD
This soup can be prepared up
to 2 days in advance and
frozen for up to 2 months.

NUTRITIONAL ANALYSIS
PER SERVING
162 calories
5.5 g protein
2.9 g fat, total
0.8 g fat, saturated
28.5 g carbohydrates
149 mg sodium
3 mg cholesterol
3.2 g fibre

TIPS
Use low-sodium, MSG-free
soup stock in powder form,
tetra packs, or cans. The
organic versions are best.

The creaminess of the Yukon Gold and sweetness of the sweet potato make for a perfect match and fabulous flavor.

2 tsp vegetable oil
1 cup chopped onions
2 tsp minced garlic
1 lb Yukon Gold potatoes, peeled and cubed (3 cups)
8 oz peeled sweet potatoes (about 3 cups), cubed
4 cups chicken or vegetable stock
1 tsp dried basil
1/8 tsp each salt and freshly ground black pepper
1/2 cup low-fat milk

GARNISH
1/4 cup chopped fresh basil or parsley

1. In a nonstick saucepan sprayed with cooking spray, heat oil over medium heat; cook onions and garlic for 5 minutes or until onions begin to brown. Stir in potatoes, stock, basil, and salt and pepper. Bring to a boil. Reduce heat to a simmer, cover, and cook for 20 minutes or until potatoes are tender.
2. In a food processor or blender, purée soup with milk. Serve sprinkled with basil.

sweet pea soup

This soup has a sweet, fresh flavor. I make it all year round and serve with a dollop of sour cream in each bowl.

2 tsp vegetable oil
1 cup chopped onions
1-1/2 tsp minced garlic
4 cups frozen green peas
3 cups chicken or vegetable stock
1 cup diced peeled potatoes
1/8 tsp each salt and freshly ground black pepper

GARNISH
2 tbsp low-fat sour cream

1. In a nonstick saucepan sprayed with cooking spray, heat oil over medium heat; cook onions and garlic for 5 minutes until onions are soft and lightly browned. Stir in remaining ingredients. Bring to a boil. Reduce heat to a simmer, cover, and cook for 15 minutes.
2. In batches, purée the soup in a blender or food processor until smooth. Serve garnished with a dollop of sour cream.

PREP: 10 mins.
COOK: About 20 mins.

MAKES 6 SERVINGS

MAKE AHEAD
This soup can be made up to 2 days in advance and frozen for up to 2 months. Add more stock when reheating.

NUTRITIONAL ANALYSIS PER SERVING
146 calories
7.7 g protein
3.2 g fat, total
0.9 g fat, saturated
21.5 g carbohydrates
215 mg sodium
4 mg cholesterol
5.4 g fibre

TIPS
Chopped frozen onions, now sold in supermarkets, are handy if you're in a hurry. Keeping a jar of minced garlic in your refrigerator is also a good idea. I use double the amount I would if using fresh garlic since the purchased minced garlic is less intense.

PREP: About 15 mins.
COOK: About 38 mins.

MAKES 8 SERVINGS

MAKE AHEAD
This soup can be made up to
2 days in advance, but don't
add the macaroni until
reheating the soup. Soup can
be frozen for up to 3 months.

NUTRITIONAL ANALYSIS
PER SERVING
170 calories
8.2 g protein
7.2 g fat, total
2.1 g fat, saturated
22 g carbohydrates
370 mg sodium
7 mg cholesterol
4.2 g fibre

TIPS
If you don't want the soup to
thicken, omit the macaroni.
Tomato paste can now be
found in tubes instead of the
usual small tins.

vegetable minestrone with parmesan cheese and pesto

The pesto adds a real pick-me-up to the traditional minestrone.

2 tsp vegetable oil
1-1/2 cups chopped onions
2 tsp minced garlic
1 cup chopped carrots
5 cups chicken or vegetable stock
1 can (19 oz) whole tomatoes with juice
1 cup diced peeled potatoes
1 cup rinsed and drained canned chick-peas
2 tbsp tomato paste
2-1/2 tsp dried basil
1 tsp dried oregano
2 bay leaves
1/8 tsp each salt and freshly ground black pepper
1/4 cup macaroni
1/4 cup grated Parmesan cheese
1/4 cup Rose's Light Pesto (see page 184) or store-bought

GARNISH
1/4 cup chopped fresh parsley

1. In a large nonstick saucepan sprayed with cooking spray, heat oil over medium heat; cook onions and garlic for 8 minutes or just until onions are tender and lightly browned. Stir in carrots; cook for 5 minutes. Stir in remaining ingredients, except macaroni, cheese, and pesto. Bring to a boil. Reduce heat to a simmer, cover, and cook for 20 minutes or just until potatoes are tender.
2. Stir in macaroni; cook covered for 5 minutes or until macaroni is tender but firm.
3. Add cheese and pesto. Remove bay leaves. Serve soup garnished with parsley.

tortilla, sautéed corn, and plum tomato soup

The garnishes for this soup—sliced flour tortillas, sour cream, diced plum tomatoes, and chopped fresh coriander—make it a real Tex Mex favorite, as well as a beautiful-looking soup. It's a great starter to fajitas, burritos, or quesadillas.

2 tsp vegetable oil
1 cup chopped onions
1/2 cup chopped sweet green peppers
2 tsp minced garlic
1 cup drained canned corn
3-1/2 cups chicken or vegetable stock
2-1/2 cups diced plum tomatoes (about 4)
1/2 cup rinsed and drained canned black beans
1/2 tsp hot pepper sauce
1/4 tsp each salt and freshly ground black pepper

GARNISH
1 cup thinly sliced flavored flour tortillas
1/3 cup chopped fresh coriander
1/4 cup low-fat sour cream

1. In a nonstick saucepan sprayed with cooking spray, heat oil over medium heat; cook onions, green peppers, and garlic for 5 minutes or until onions are golden. Stir in corn; cook for 5 minutes or until corn begins to brown.

2. Stir in stock, 2 cups of plum tomatoes, black beans, and hot pepper sauce. Bring to a boil. Reduce heat to a simmer; cook for 15 minutes. Stir in salt and pepper. Serve soup sprinkled with garnishes and remaining plum tomatoes.

PREP: About 15 mins.
COOK: About 25 mins.

MAKES 6 SERVINGS

MAKE AHEAD
This soup can be prepared up to 1 day in advance and frozen for up to 1 month. Garnish just before serving.

NUTRITIONAL ANALYSIS PER SERVING
144 calories
6.8 g protein
4.1 g fat, total
1.1 g fat, saturated
20 g carbohydrates
320 mg sodium
4.1 mg cholesterol
3.1 g fibre

TIPS
I buy flavored tortillas in bulk and freeze them. To defrost, place the entire package in the microwave and heat on High for 30 seconds or just until you can break away the number you need. Refreeze the remainder. The different colors add interest to any meal.

sweet potato and pepper soup

The combination of grilled peppers and sweet potatoes produces a sweet, velvety-textured soup and provides excellent nutrition. The peppers have three times more vitamin C than an orange.

4 sweet peppers, any color
2 tsp vegetable oil
1 cup chopped onions
1/2 cup diced carrots
2 tsp minced garlic
1 tsp dried basil
3-3/4 cups chicken or vegetable stock
2 cups chopped peeled sweet potatoes
1/4 tsp salt

GARNISH
1/4 cup low-fat plain yogurt

1. Under a preheated broiler or over medium-high heat on a grill, cook peppers for 15 minutes, turning occasionally, or until charred on all sides. Cool. Peel, stem, core, and slice.
2. In a nonstick saucepan sprayed with cooking spray, heat oil over medium heat; cook onions, carrots, garlic, and basil for 5 minutes or until onions are browned. Stir in stock, sweet potatoes, and peppers. Bring to a boil. Reduce heat to a simmer, cover, and cook for 25 minutes or until potatoes are tender.
3. In batches, purée soup in a blender or food processor. Return to saucepan. Stir in salt. Serve soup garnished with a dollop of yogurt.

PREP: About 10 mins.
COOK: About 45 mins.

MAKES 6 SERVINGS

MAKE AHEAD
This soup can be made up to 2 days in advance or frozen for up to 3 months. Add more stock when reheating.

NUTRITIONAL ANALYSIS PER SERVING
143 calories
6 g protein
3 g fat, total
0.5 g fat, saturated
23 g carbohydrates
420 mg sodium
0.6 mg cholesterol
3.6 g fibre

TIPS
If you're rushed and want to peel the peppers quickly, just run them under cold water as you peel them. I often grill several sweet peppers when they're in season, peel, core, and slice them, and freeze them in small containers for later use. They freeze well.

black bean soup

This creamy, rich-tasting soup is very nutritious. I like to serve it garnished with low-fat sour cream, diced plum tomatoes, or a sprinkle of shredded Cheddar cheese.

1 can (19 oz) black beans, rinsed and drained
2 tsp vegetable oil
1 cup chopped onions
1 cup chopped carrots
2 tsp minced garlic
2-1/2 cups chicken or vegetable stock
1/2 tsp granulated sugar
3/4 tsp cumin

GARNISH
1/4 cup chopped fresh coriander or parsley

1. Set aside 1/2 cup of black beans.
2. In a nonstick saucepan sprayed with cooking spray, heat oil over medium heat; cook onions, carrots, and garlic for 5 minutes, stirring occasionally, or until softened. Stir in remaining beans, stock, sugar, and cumin. Bring to a boil. Reduce heat to medium-low, cover, and cook for 15 minutes or until carrots are tender.
3. In batches, purée soup in a blender or food processor. Return to saucepan. Stir in reserved beans. Serve soup sprinkled with coriander.

PREP: About 10 mins.
COOK: About 20 mins.

MAKES 4 SERVINGS

MAKE AHEAD
Make this soup up to 2 days in advance or freeze for up to 3 months. Add more stock when reheating.

NUTRITIONAL ANALYSIS
PER SERVING
140 calories
8.2 g protein
3.2 g fat, total
0.2 g fat, saturated
25 g carbohydrates
420 mg sodium
0 mg cholesterol
7.1 g fibre

TIP
If you can't find canned black beans, cook your own using the quick-soak method. Boil in enough water to cover 1 cup dried beans for 3 minutes. Remove from heat, cover, and let sit for 1 hour. Drain, replace water, and simmer just until cooked, about 40 minutes.

yellow split pea soup

If you're tired of green split pea soup, this yellow split pea version will be welcome. The peas are filled with fibre and complex carbohydrates. The potatoes give the soup its creaminess.

2 tsp vegetable oil
1 cup chopped onions
1 cup chopped carrots
1 cup chopped celery
2 tsp minced garlic
5 cups chicken or vegetable stock
1 cup diced peeled potatoes
1 cup dried yellow split peas
1/8 tsp salt and pepper

GARNISH
1/4 cup chopped green onions
1/4 cup low-fat plain yogurt (optional)

1. In a nonstick saucepan sprayed with cooking spray, heat oil over medium-high heat; cook onions, carrots, celery, and garlic for 5 minutes or until vegetables are softened and starting to brown. Stir in remaining ingredients. Bring to a boil. Reduce heat to medium-low, cover, and cook for 30 to 35 minutes or until split peas are tender.

2. In batches, purée soup in a blender or food processor. Serve soup sprinkled with green onions and (if using) a dollop of yogurt.

PREP: About 10 mins.
COOK: About 35 mins.

MAKES 6 SERVINGS

MAKE AHEAD
This soup can be made up to 3 days in advance or frozen for up to 3 months. Add more stock when reheating.

NUTRITIONAL ANALYSIS PER SERVING
200 calories
14 g protein
4.1 g fat, total
0.7 g fat, saturated
40 g carbohydrates
480 mg sodium
0 mg cholesterol
9.1 g fibre

TIPS
Split peas are great to use in soups because they don't have to be soaked and they cook in a relatively short time. For a creamier texture, try using Yukon Gold potatoes instead of regular white potatoes.

creamy pumpkin soup

I love serving this comfort soup around Halloween and on holidays such as Thanksgiving and Christmas. During the fall, try using fresh pumpkin. Roast a small pumpkin at 400°F until tender, about 45 minutes.

2 tsp vegetable oil
1-1/2 cups chopped onions
1-1/2 cups chopped carrots
1 tsp minced garlic
3-1/2 cups chicken or vegetable stock
1-1/2 cups canned pumpkin purée
1/2 tsp cinnamon
1/2 tsp ginger
1/8 tsp nutmeg
1 cup low-fat milk
2 tsp liquid honey

GARNISH
Chopped fresh parsley

1. In a nonstick saucepan sprayed with cooking spray, heat oil over medium-high heat; cook onions, carrots, and garlic for 10 minutes, stirring frequently, or until onions are softened and browned. Stir in stock, pumpkin, cinnamon, ginger, and nutmeg. Bring to a boil. Reduce heat to low, cover, and cook for 20 minutes or until carrot is tender.
2. In batches, purée soup in a blender or food processor. Return soup to saucepan. Stir in milk and honey. Gently reheat. Serve soup garnished with parsley.

PREP: About 10 mins.
COOK: About 30 mins.

MAKES 4 SERVINGS

MAKE AHEAD
This soup can be made up to 2 days in advance or frozen for up to 3 months. Add more stock when reheating.

NUTRITIONAL ANALYSIS PER SERVING
172 calories
9.2 g protein
4.4 g fat, total
1 g fat, saturated
24 g carbohydrates
480 mg sodium
2.4 mg cholesterol
6.7 g fibre

TIP
For a decorative presentation, serve this soup in a seeded pumpkin shell. When very small pumpkins are available, I remove the top and seeds and serve a soup-filled pumpkin to each guest.

wild mushroom soup

Anyone who doesn't love mushrooms will after trying this smooth soup. It is filled with the aroma and taste of whatever mushrooms you select. Mushroom soup in a restaurant is usually made with cream and butter. This soup contains only a small amount of vegetable oil.

2 tsp vegetable oil
1 cup chopped onions
2 tsp minced garlic
1/2 cup diced carrots
6 cups diced wild mushrooms (about 12 oz)
3-1/2 cups chicken or vegetable stock
1-1/2 cups chopped peeled potatoes
1/2 tsp dried rosemary
1/2 tsp dried thyme
1/2 tsp salt
1/4 tsp freshly ground black pepper
1/2 cup low-fat milk
3 tbsp grated Parmesan cheese

GARNISH
1/4 cup chopped fresh parsley

1. In a nonstick saucepan sprayed with cooking spray, heat oil over medium-high heat; cook onions and garlic for 5 minutes. Stir in carrots; cook for 3 minutes. Stir in mushrooms; cook for 10 minutes or until mushroom liquid has evaporated and mushrooms are browned.
2. Stir in stock, potatoes, rosemary, thyme, salt, and pepper. Bring to a boil. Reduce heat to a simmer, cover, and cook for 15 minutes or until potatoes and carrots are tender.
3. In batches, purée soup in a blender or food processor. Return to saucepan. Stir in milk and Parmesan cheese. Serve soup garnished with parsley.

PREP: About 15 mins.
COOK: About 33 mins.

MAKES 6 SERVINGS

MAKE AHEAD
Make this soup up to 2 days in advance or freeze for up to 2 months. Add more stock when reheating.

NUTRITIONAL ANALYSIS
PER SERVING
124 calories
7.1 g protein
3.5 g fat, total
0.8 g fat, saturated
16 g carbohydrates
390 mg sodium
3.7 mg cholesterol
2.1 g fibre

TIPS
I have often made this soup using a combination of portobello, brown, oyster, and regular mushrooms. These are the most affordable. If your pocketbook allows you to buy them, porcini, chanterelles, or shiitakes make this soup sensational.

udon noodle soup with chicken and shrimp

Udon noodles are long, round, white noodles that have a wonderfully dense texture. This soup has to be one of my all-time favorites—it's not only delicious, but also quick to make.

4 oz boneless skinless chicken breast (about 1 breast), diced

2 tsp minced gingerroot

2 tsp minced garlic

6 cups chicken or beef stock

2 tbsp low-sodium soy sauce

6 oz fresh udon noodles

2 cups sliced bok choy

1/2 cup sliced snow peas

4 oz deveined peeled shrimp, chopped

1 cup bean sprouts

2 large green onions, chopped

GARNISH

2 tsp sesame oil

3 tbsp chopped fresh parsley

1. In a nonstick wok or large nonstick saucepan sprayed with cooking spray, cook chicken over medium-high heat for 4 minutes or until meat is barely cooked through. Add gingerroot and garlic and cook for 1 more minute. Set aside.

2. In a large saucepan, bring stock and soy sauce to a boil. Add udon noodles; return to a boil. Reduce heat to medium-high; cook for 4 minutes or until noodles are tender. Add bok choy, snow peas, and shrimp; cook for 2 minutes or until shrimp are pink and snow peas are tender-crisp.

3. Add chicken, bean sprouts, and green onions; cook until heated through. Serve soup drizzled with sesame oil and sprinkled with parsley.

PREP: About 15 mins.
COOK: About 12 mins.

MAKES 6 SERVINGS

MAKE AHEAD
Prepare up to 1 day in advance. It's best not to freeze soup containing udon noodles.

NUTRITIONAL ANALYSIS
PER SERVING
207 calories
12 g protein
7 g fat, total
2.1 g fat, saturated
23 g carbohydrates
380 mg sodium
46 mg cholesterol
1 g fibre

TIP
To keep bean sprouts fresh longer, store them in water in the refrigerator.

super quick

PREP: About 10 mins.
COOK: About 3 mins.

MAKES 6 SERVINGS

MAKE AHEAD
Prepare soup, without the
noodles, up to 1 day in
advance. Add noodles just
before serving. Soup can be
frozen for up to 2 months.

NUTRITIONAL ANALYSIS
PER SERVING
139 calories
14 g protein
5.1 g fat, total
0.9 g fat, saturated
9.2 g carbohydrates
740 mg sodium
13 mg cholesterol
0.8 g fibre

TIPS
Miso paste comes in different
colors and textures and varies
in taste. Lighter paste is
sweeter; darker paste is
stronger since it's been fermented longer. The colors are
white, yellow, brown, and
red. I like to use the yellow
paste. Nori (seaweed) sheets
can be found in supermarkets
that sell takeout sushi.

miso soup with chow mein noodles, chicken, and tofu

I never have a Japanese meal without enjoying a bowl of miso soup. It's delicious and helps fill me comfortably before the sushi comes. I never realized how easy it is to make miso soup at home. This homemade version is even better than the miso soup served in restaurants. Miso paste can be found in some supermarkets in the refrigerator section, often where the yogurt and other soy products are, or at a specialty or health food shop.

5 cups chicken or vegetable stock
1/4 cup yellow miso paste
1 tbsp low-sodium soy sauce
2 tsp sesame oil
2 tsp minced garlic
2 tsp minced gingerroot
3 oz medium-firm or firm tofu, cubed
2 oz fresh chow mein noodles (not the dry kind)
1 sheet nori, cut into thin strips
1/2 tsp hot Asian chili sauce
3 oz cooked chicken or deveined peeled shrimp, diced

GARNISH
1/3 cup chopped green onions

In a large saucepan, whisk together stock, miso, soy sauce, sesame oil, garlic, and gingerroot. Bring to a boil. Reduce heat to a simmer. Stir in tofu, noodles, nori, and chili sauce; cook for 3 minutes or until noodles are tender. Stir in chicken. Serve soup sprinkled with green onions.

southwest smoked chicken chowder

The smell and taste of this soup make it a Tex Mex favorite. You'll love the texture and barbe-cued taste sautéing gives to the corn. If you're a "hot lover," add as much hot sauce as you like!

2 sweet red, yellow, or orange peppers (roast peppers while cooking soup)
2 tsp vegetable oil
1 cup chopped onions
2 tsp minced garlic
1 cup drained canned corn
4 cups chicken stock
2 cups cubed peeled potatoes
1 cup rinsed and drained canned black beans
1 cup chopped smoked chicken or turkey
1/2 tsp hot pepper sauce
1/8 tsp each salt and freshly ground black pepper

GARNISH
1/4 cup chopped fresh coriander or parsley

1. Under a preheated broiler or over medium-high heat on a grill, cook peppers for 15 minutes, turning frequently, or until charred on all sides. Cool. Peel, stem, core, and chop them.
2. In a nonstick saucepan sprayed with cooking spray, heat oil over medium-high heat; cook onions and garlic for 3 minutes. Stir in corn; cook for 5 minutes, stirring occasionally, or until browned. Stir in stock and potatoes. Bring to a boil. Reduce heat to medium-low, cover, and cook for 10 minutes or until potatoes are tender.
3. Stir in peppers, black beans, chicken, hot pepper sauce, and salt and pepper; cook for 5 minutes or until heated through. Serve soup garnished with coriander.

PREP: About 15 mins.
COOK: About 25 mins.

MAKES 6 SERVINGS

MAKE AHEAD
Prepare up to 1 day in advance. Freeze for up to 1 month. Add more stock, if necessary, when reheating.

NUTRITIONAL ANALYSIS PER SERVING
178 calories
11 g protein
3.3 g fat, total
0.6 g fat, saturated
26 g carbohydrates
684 mg sodium
10 mg cholesterol
4.7 g fibre

TIPS
You can use bottled roasted peppers as long as they're not marinated in oil. About 8 ounces replaces 2 sweet peppers. If you can find them, use thicker cuts of smoked chicken. Smoked chicken can be replaced with roasted chicken or turkey cubes or slices.

thai seafood stew

PREP: About 15 mins.
COOK: About 15 mins.

MAKES 6 SERVINGS

MAKE AHEAD
The sauce can be made up to
1 day in advance. Seafood
should be cooked just before
serving.

NUTRITIONAL ANALYSIS
PER SERVING
172 calories
21 g protein
5 g fat, total
1.5 g fat, saturated
10.8 g carbohydrates
290 mg sodium
82 mg cholesterol
1.4 g fibre

TIPS
If you don't have fish stock,
which can be bought fresh or
in powdered form, clam juice
is a great substitute. If you
have neither, substitute
chicken stock. If you prefer to
remove the lemon grass, then
cut it into larger pieces.
Always remove large pieces
of lemon grass before serving.

This stew is wonderful served with salad and a French baguette for dipping. The light coconut milk gives a subtle flavor and contains 75 percent less fat and calories than regular coconut milk.

2 tsp vegetable oil
1 cup chopped onions
2 tsp minced garlic
2 cups chopped plum tomatoes
1/2 cup fish stock or clam juice
1 tbsp fish sauce or oyster sauce
1 tbsp packed brown sugar
1 stalk lemon grass, finely chopped or 2 tsp grated lemon rind
16 mussels
8 oz deveined peeled shrimp
8 oz scallops
1/2 cup light coconut milk
1 tsp Asian hot sauce

GARNISH
1/4 cup chopped fresh coriander or parsley

1. In a large nonstick saucepan sprayed with cooking spray, heat oil over medium heat; cook onions and garlic for 5 minutes. Stir in tomatoes, stock, fish sauce, brown sugar, and lemon grass. Bring to a boil. Reduce heat to a simmer, cover, and cook for 5 minutes.
2. Stir in seafood, cover, and cook for 3 minutes or just until mussels open and seafood is barely cooked. Do not overcook. Stir in coconut milk and hot sauce; cook for 1 minute. Serve soup sprinkled with coriander.

salmon and corn chowder

With a salad and some French bread, this chowder is dinner for me. It's nutritious, delicious, and low in fat. Salmon contains omega-3 fatty acids that help reduce blood cholesterol and protect the body against free radicals, which may cause cancer.

1 cup drained canned corn

2 tsp vegetable oil

1-1/2 cups diced fennel

3/4 cup diced onions

1/2 cup diced carrots

1 tsp minced garlic

2-1/2 cups fish or chicken stock

1-1/2 cups low-fat milk

2 tbsp all-purpose flour

1 tsp Dijon mustard

8 oz skinless salmon fillet, diced

1 tbsp fresh lemon juice

GARNISH

1/4 cup diced bottled roasted red peppers

1/4 cup chopped fresh dill or parsley

1. In a nonstick skillet sprayed with cooking spray, cook corn over medium heat for 8 minutes, stirring often, or until slightly charred. Set aside.
2. In the same pan, heat oil over medium heat; cook fennel, onions, carrots, and garlic for 5 minutes or until vegetables start to brown. Stir in stock and reserved corn. Bring to a boil. Reduce heat to a simmer, cover, and cook for 15 minutes.
3. In a bowl, whisk together milk, flour, and mustard; stir into chowder. Cook 2 minutes, stirring, or until slightly thickened. Stir in salmon; cook for 2 minutes uncovered, or until salmon is cooked through. Stir in lemon juice. Serve soup garnished with red peppers and dill.

PREP: About 15 mins.
COOK: About 32 mins.

MAKES 6 SERVINGS

MAKE AHEAD
You can make this soup 1 day ahead right up to the point before the salmon is added, which is best done just before serving. Freeze it for up to 1 month.

NUTRITIONAL ANALYSIS
PER SERVING
170 calories
13 g protein
7 g fat, total
1.6 g fat, saturated
16 g carbohydrates
320 mg sodium
26 mg cholesterol
2.2 g fibre

TIPS
For fish stock, either make your own, use canned stock or bouillon cubes, or try bottled clam juice. If you don't have fennel, substitute half celery and half onion.

tex mex beef and bean soup

PREP: About 15 mins.
COOK: About 30 mins.

MAKES 6 SERVINGS

MAKE AHEAD
This soup can be prepared
up to 2 days in advance and
frozen for up to 2 months.
Garnish only when ready
to serve.

NUTRITIONAL ANALYSIS
PER SERVING
262 calories
16.8 g protein
7.2 g fat, total
2.2 g fat, saturated
32.6 g carbohydrates
463 mg sodium
15 mg cholesterol
10.5 g fibre

Most Tex Mex dishes are delicious but high in fat because often they are deep-fried and contain large amounts of cheese and fatty meats. This soup has the great flavor of, but much less fat than, many Tex Mex dishes.

2 tsp vegetable oil
1 cup chopped onions
2 tsp minced garlic
8 oz extra lean ground beef
1 can (14 oz) diced tomatoes
2 cups rinsed and drained canned red kidney beans
1-1/2 cups beef or chicken stock
1 cup tomato pasta sauce
1 tsp dried basil
1 tsp chili powder
1/2 tsp dried oregano

GARNISH
3 tbsp shredded light Cheddar cheese
3 tbsp chopped fresh coriander or parsley
2 tbsp low-fat sour cream

1. In a large nonstick saucepan sprayed with cooking spray, heat oil over medium heat; cook onions and garlic for 5 minutes or until onions begin to brown. Stir in beef; cook for 5 minutes, or until it is no longer pink, stirring to break up beef.
2. Stir in remaining ingredients, except garnishes. Bring soup to a boil. Reduce heat to a simmer, cover, and cook for 20 minutes, stirring occasionally. Serve soup with garnishes (if using).

beef and rice soup

In the colder months, this soup is the perfect comfort food. I serve it with a salad and some crusty French bread. Don't use stewing beef since it takes too long to become tender.

8 oz boneless inside round steak, diced
2 tbsp all-purpose flour
2 tsp vegetable oil
1 cup chopped onions
1 cup chopped sweet green peppers
1/3 cup diced carrots
2 tsp minced garlic
1/3 cup white rice
4 cups beef stock
3 cups chopped plum tomatoes (about 5)
1 tbsp packed brown sugar
1-1/2 tsp dried basil
1 tsp dried oregano
1 bay leaf
1/4 tsp each salt and freshly ground pepper

GARNISH
3 tbsp grated Parmesan cheese
1/4 cup chopped fresh parsley

1. Dust beef with flour. In a nonstick saucepan sprayed with cooking spray, heat oil over medium-high heat; cook beef for 5 minutes or until browned. Remove beef from pan.
2. Wipe pan out. Spray with cooking spray. Return pan to medium heat; cook onions, green peppers, carrots, and garlic for 8 minutes. Stir in rice; cook for 1 minute, stirring. Stir in beef and remaining ingredients, except garnishes. Bring to a boil. Reduce heat to a simmer, cover, and cook for 10 minutes or until rice is tender.
3. Remove bay leaf. Serve soup sprinkled with Parmesan and parsley (if using).

PREP: About 15 mins.
COOK: About 25 mins.

MAKES 6 SERVINGS

MAKE AHEAD
Cook up to 1 day in advance or freeze for up to 2 months, adding more stock when reheating.

NUTRITIONAL ANALYSIS PER SERVING
136 calories
12 g protein
4 g fat, total
0.5 g fat, saturated
17 g carbohydrates
320 mg sodium
20 mg cholesterol
1.2 g fibre

TIPS
You can use chicken or pork instead of beef. For a twist, replace the rice with another grain such as couscous, quinoa, or barley. Check the cooking times for different grains. You can use canned plum tomatoes instead of fresh. You will need about one and a half 19-ounce cans or one 28-ounce can.

cabbage beef barley soup

PREP: About 15 mins.
COOK: About 50 mins.

MAKES 8 SERVINGS

MAKE AHEAD
Cook up to 2 days in advance
or freeze for up to 2 months,
adding more stock when
reheating.

NUTRITIONAL ANALYSIS
PER SERVING
138 calories
11 g protein
2 g fat, total
0.7 g fat, saturated
19 g carbohydrates
460 mg sodium
15 mg cholesterol
4 g fibre

TIP
For the barley, substitute
other grains such as rice,
couscous, quinoa or pasta.
You may need to adjust the
cooking time, depending on
your substitution.

This classic European soup will continue to live on through the decades. Instead of using stewing beef, I like to use a more tender cut that doesn't have to cook for so long. Cabbage is a part of the cruciferous vegetable family and is a powerful antioxidant, helping in the fight against colon and other cancers.

8 oz boneless inside round steak, cut into 1/2-inch cubes
2 tbsp all-purpose flour
2 tsp vegetable oil
1 cup chopped onions
1 cup chopped carrots
1/2 cup chopped celery
1 tsp minced garlic
2 cups shredded cabbage
1 can (19 oz) whole tomatoes with juice
5 cups beef or chicken stock
1 cup diced peeled potatoes
1/3 cup pearl barley
1-1/2 tsp caraway seeds
1/2 tsp hot pepper sauce
1/4 tsp each salt and freshly ground black pepper
2 tbsp fresh lemon juice

GARNISH
3 tbsp chopped fresh parsley

1. Dust beef with flour. In a nonstick saucepan sprayed with cooking spray, add 1 tsp oil and cook beef over medium-high for 5 minutes or until browned. Remove beef from pan.

2. Wipe pan out. Spray pan with cooking spray and add remaining 1 tsp oil. Return pan to medium heat; cook onions, carrots, celery, and garlic for 8 to 10 minutes, stirring occasionally. Stir in cabbage; cook for 2 minutes, stirring, or until cabbage is wilted.

3. Stir in beef and remaining ingredients, except lemon juice and parsley. Bring to a boil, crushing tomatoes with the back of a spoon. Reduce heat to low, cover, and cook for 35 to 40 minutes or until barley is tender. Stir in lemon juice. Serve soup garnished with parsley.

wraps

PREP: About 10 mins.
COOK: About 12 mins.

MAKES 6 SERVINGS

MAKE AHEAD
Hummus can be made up to
3 days in advance. Stuff the
pitas up to 4 hours before
serving.

NUTRITIONAL ANALYSIS
PER SERVING
222 calories
5.5 g protein
1.6 g fat, total
0.4 g fat, saturated
8.3 g carbohydrates
140 mg sodium
33 mg cholesterol
0.7 g fibre

TIPS
Buy only roasted peppers
packed in water, not oil, and
freeze any leftover contents
of the jar.

portobello mushroom wraps with red pepper hummus and goat cheese

When you're in the mood for a vegetarian alternative, look no further than this. Portobellos are called the meat of the vegetable family. They have a firm and delicious texture and taste and are wonderful with hummus and goat cheese.

RED PEPPER HUMMUS
1/2 cup rinsed and drained canned chick-peas
1 oz bottled roasted sweet red peppers (1/4 sweet red pepper, roasted)
2 tbsp chopped fresh parsley
1-1/2 tbsp tahini (sesame seed paste)
1 tbsp fresh lemon juice
1 tbsp water
2 tsp olive oil
1/4 tsp hot pepper sauce

WRAPS
3 large portobello mushroom caps, wiped (stems removed)
3 medium-sized pita breads, sliced in half
2 oz goat cheese, crumbled

GARNISH
Lettuce
Sliced tomatoes
Sliced onions

1. To make hummus: In a food processor, combine all ingredients; purée until smooth.
2. To make wraps: On either a barbecue or a nonstick grill pan sprayed with cooking spray, grill mushrooms over medium-high heat for 12 minutes, turning halfway, or until tender and grill-marked. Spray mushrooms with vegetable spray if they look dry. Slice in half.
3. Spread inside of pita halves with hummus. Place half mushroom cap in pita, sprinkle with cheese, and garnish (if using).

seafood pitas

Tiny shrimp taste great with pesto sauce in a fresh pita. If you can't find cocktail shrimp, buy larger shrimp and dice them.

FILLING

12 oz cooked baby shrimp

1/2 cup finely diced sweet red peppers

1/4 cup finely diced green onions

2 tbsp Rose's Light Pesto (see page 184) or store-bought

1 tbsp light mayonnaise

1/8 tsp each salt and freshly ground black pepper

4 medium-sized pita breads, cut in half

1. To make filling: In a bowl, stir together all ingredients.
2. Stuff filling into pita halves.

super
quick

PREP: About 15 mins.

MAKES 8 SERVINGS

MAKE AHEAD
Prepare filling up to 4 hours early, but don't fill pitas until 1 hour before serving time.

NUTRITIONAL ANALYSIS
PER SERVING
140 calories
10.9 g protein
3.3 g fat, total
0.7 g fat, saturated
16.7 g carbohydrates
280 mg sodium
67 mg cholesterol
1.4 g fibre

crabmeat and rice wraps

PREP: About 15 mins.
COOK: About 40 mins.

MAKES 8 SERVINGS

MAKE AHEAD
Filling can be prepared
up to 1 day in advance. Fill
wraps and serve at room
temperature.

NUTRITIONAL ANALYSIS
PER SERVING
255 calories
17 g protein
7 g fat, total
3.3 g fat, saturated
30 g carbohydrates
290 mg sodium
36 mg cholesterol
2 g fibre

TIPS
Using an exotic mushroom in
this recipe highlights the
other ingredients. I prefer
oyster mushrooms in this
dish. If wild rice is not available, use white rice or a combination of rices, keeping in
mind that wild rice takes at
least 35 minutes to cook,
whereas white rice takes only
12 minutes.

This delicious wrap has a unique taste. Wild rice and sautéed mushrooms with a cheesy crab-meat filling make this an outstanding sandwich. Surimi, which is imitation crabmeat, is inexpensive, readily available, and delicious. It's made from a variety of white fish, mainly pollock.

FILLING
1-1/4 cups chicken stock
1/4 cup wild rice (cook rice while preparing rest of filling)
1 tsp vegetable oil
1/3 cup chopped onions
1 tsp minced garlic
1 cup chopped mushrooms
1/2 cup smooth light ricotta cheese
1 oz light cream cheese, cubed
2 tbsp grated Parmesan cheese
4 oz cooked crabmeat or surimi, chopped
3 tbsp chopped fresh dill
3 tbsp chopped green onions
1/8 tsp each salt and freshly ground black pepper

4 large flour tortillas

1. To make filling: In a small saucepan, combine stock and rice. Bring to a boil. Reduce heat to medium-low. Cover and cook for 35 to 40 minutes or until rice is tender. Drain any excess liquid. Set aside.
2. In a nonstick skillet sprayed with cooking spray, heat oil over medium-high heat; cook onions and garlic for 3 minutes or until browned. Stir in mushrooms; cook for 5 to 8 minutes or until browned and all moisture has evaporated. Add cheeses and stir until melted. Remove from heat. Stir in crabmeat, dill, green onions, salt and pepper, and rice.
3. Place one-quarter of rice mixture in centre of a tortilla. Roll bottom of tortilla up and over filling tightly, fold in both sides, and continue to roll. Cut in half. Repeat with remaining tortillas and filling.

tuna, feta, and dill wraps

Forget the traditional tuna sandwich. Wrap and roll with fresh dill, lemon juice, and Dijon mustard for a delicious twist on the traditional tuna sandwich.

FILLING

1 can (170 g) flaked water-packed tuna, drained

3 tbsp light mayonnaise

2 tbsp light sour cream

1/2 cup chopped sweet red peppers

1/3 cup chopped sweet Vidalia onion

1/3 cup chopped celery

1/4 cup chopped black olives

1/4 cup chopped fresh dill

1 oz feta cheese, crumbled

2 tbsp lemon juice

1 tsp minced garlic

1 tsp Dijon mustard

Pinch salt and pepper

4 large flour tortillas
4 pieces leafy lettuce

1. To make filling: In a medium-sized bowl, mix all filling ingredients until well blended.
2. Place one-quarter of the filling in centre of a tortilla; top with a piece of lettuce. Fold up bottom of tortilla, fold in both sides, and continue to roll. Cut in half. Repeat with remaining tortillas and filling.

super quick

PREP: About 15 mins.

MAKES 8 SERVINGS

MAKE AHEAD
Prepare filling up to 1 day in advance. It's best to make the wraps no more than 2 hours before serving.

NUTRITIONAL ANALYSIS PER SERVING
170 calories
9 g protein
5 g fat, total
1.3 g fat, saturated
22 g carbohydrates
370 mg sodium
9 mg cholesterol
1.7 g fibre

TIPS
Be sure to buy tuna packed in water. Tuna packed in oil has double the calories and six times the fat! Flaked tuna is easier to use.

chicken and peanut sauce wraps

PREP: About 15 mins.
COOK: About 14 mins.

MAKES 8 SERVINGS

MAKE AHEAD
Grill chicken up to 1 day
before or freeze extra cooked
breasts for up to 2 months.
Prepare sauce up to 3 days in
advance. Wrap tortillas up to
2 hours before serving.

NUTRITIONAL ANALYSIS
PER SERVING
186 calories
11 g protein
6 g fat, total
1.3 g fat, saturated
22 g carbohydrates
308 mg sodium
16 mg cholesterol
0.9 g fibre

TIP
Replace the chicken with
good quality steak, stir-fried
tofu, or shrimp.

Whenever I have guests over for an informal meal (which is all the time), I love to serve these wraps. They're easy to prepare, absolutely delicious, and can be prepared ahead of time. You can always warm the tortillas by wrapping them in foil and heating in the oven at 425°F for 3 minutes.

8 oz boneless skinless chicken breast (about 2 breasts)
2 oz capellini pasta

SAUCE
2 tbsp smooth natural peanut butter
2 tbsp water
1 tbsp low-sodium soy sauce
1 tbsp rice wine vinegar
1 tbsp liquid honey
2 tsp sesame oil
1/2 tsp minced garlic
1/2 tsp minced gingerroot
1/4 tsp Asian hot sauce

1 cup chopped sweet red peppers
1/2 cup chopped green onions
1/4 cup chopped fresh coriander

4 large flour tortillas

1. Preheat grill or grill pan. Spray with cooking spray. Grill chicken over medium-high heat for 12 minutes, turning once, or until cooked through. Meanwhile, boil pasta until al dente, approximately 2 minutes. Drain, rinse with cold water, and cut into smaller pieces. Set aside.
2. To make sauce: In a small food processor or bowl, beat sauce ingredients together until smooth.
3. Slice warm chicken thinly. Combine chicken, capellini, red peppers, green onions, and coriander with sauce.
4. Place one-quarter of chicken mixture in centre of a tortilla. Roll bottom of tortilla up and over filling tightly, fold in both sides, and continue to roll. Cut in half. Repeat with remaining tortillas and chicken mixture.

chicken caesar wraps

Everyone loves Caesar salads. Here's one put in a wrap. It's great tasting and perfect for lunch or summer dining.

8 oz boneless skinless chicken breast (about 2 breasts)

CAESAR DRESSING
1 egg
2 tbsp grated Parmesan cheese
2 anchovy fillets minced
2 tsp lemon juice
1/2 tsp Dijon mustard
1 tsp minced garlic
Pinch ground black pepper

3 cups torn romaine lettuce
4 large flour tortillas

1. Grill or sauté chicken in a nonstick grill pan, sprayed with vegetable oil, over medium heat for 6 minutes per side or until cooked through. Cut chicken into small cubes.
2. To make dressing: In a large bowl, combine all dressing ingredients.
3. Combine chicken and lettuce with dressing.
4. Place one-quarter of chicken mixture in centre of a tortilla. Roll bottom of tortilla up and over filling tightly, fold in both sides, and continue to roll. Cut in half. Repeat with remaining tortillas and chicken mixture.

PREP: About 15 mins.
COOK: About 12 mins.

MAKES 8 SERVINGS

MAKE AHEAD
The dressing can be made up to 3 days in advance. Cooked frozen, chicken breasts can be stored for up to 2 months. It's best to assemble these wraps just before serving.

NUTRITIONAL ANALYSIS PER SERVING
185 calories
14.7 g protein
5.2 g fat, total
1.5 g fat, saturated
22 g carbohydrates
315 mg sodium
52 mg cholesterol
1.5 g fibre

TIPS
Substitute shrimp or stir-fried tofu for the chicken.

super quick

PREP: About 15 mins.

MAKES 8 SERVINGS

MAKE AHEAD
The hummus can be prepared up to 2 days in advance, but it's best to roll the wraps no more than 2 hours before serving.

NUTRITIONAL ANALYSIS PER SERVING
278 calories
11.1 g protein
10 g fat, total
2 g fat, saturated
36 g carbohydrates
489 mg sodium
15 mg cholesterol
3.3 g fibre

TIP
For a variation, substitute smoked salmon for the turkey.

roasted turkey and hummus wraps

Hummus is easy to prepare and much lower in fat and calories than the store-bought version, which can be loaded with excess oil. Hummus is great as a spread for a wrap or sandwich and goes well with turkey.

HUMMUS
1 cup drained and rinsed chick-peas
1/4 cup water
1/4 cup tahini
2 tbsp lemon juice
1 tsp minced garlic
1-1/2 tbsp olive oil

4 large flour tortillas
1 plum tomato, sliced
4 slices Vidalia onion
4 pieces leafy lettuce
8 oz roasted turkey slices

1. To make hummus: Purée all hummus ingredients in a food processor until smooth.
2. Spread hummus on each tortilla. Place a tomato slice, an onion slice, a lettuce leaf, and one-quarter of the turkey slices over top. Roll bottom of tortilla up and over filling tightly, fold in both sides, and continue to roll. Cut in half.

pizza wraps

Forget the pizza with all that excess bread and cheese! Wrap and roll with this unique sandwich.

2 tsp vegetable oil
1-1/2 cups diced onions
2 tsp minced garlic
6 oz extra lean ground beef
1-1/2 cups tomato pasta sauce
1 tsp dried basil

6 large flavored flour tortillas
1/2 cup shredded low-fat mozzarella cheese
2 tbsp grated Parmesan cheese

1. Preheat oven to 400°F.
2. In a nonstick skillet sprayed with cooking spray, heat oil over medium-high heat; cook onions and garlic for 8 minutes or until onions are brown. Stir in ground beef; cook for 5 minutes, or until beef is no longer pink, stirring to break meat up. Stir in tomato sauce and basil; cover, and simmer for 10 minutes.
3. Divide beef mixture among the tortillas, spreading it in the centre; sprinkle with cheeses. Fold bottom half up to centre, fold in sides, and then roll. Place seam down on rimmed baking sheet.
4. Bake in centre of oven for 5 minutes or until tortillas are just warm and slightly crisp.

PREP: About 5 mins.
COOK: About 28 mins.

MAKES 6 SERVINGS

MAKE AHEAD
Prepare beef filling and cheeses up to 2 days in advance. The wraps are best baked just before serving, but they reheat well in the oven at 350°F for 5 minutes. Freeze them for up to 2 months.

NUTRITIONAL ANALYSIS PER SERVING
397 calories
18.2 g protein
13.5 g fat, total
4.3 g fat, saturated
50.7 g carbohydrates
320 mg sodium
20 mg cholesterol
2.5 g fibre

TIPS
Try replacing the ground beef with ground soy, found in the produce section of your supermarket: the soy is healthier for you and cholesterol free.

curried beef and rice wraps

PREP: 15 mins.
COOK: About 18 mins.

MAKES 12 SERVINGS

MAKE AHEAD
Prepare entire filling up to
1 day in advance. Bring to
room temperature, and then
fill wraps and heat in an oven
at 400°F for 5 minutes.

NUTRITIONAL ANALYSIS
PER SERVING
213 calories
9 g protein
4.8 g fat, total
1.4 g fat, saturated
38 g carbohydrates
254 mg sodium
14 mg cholesterol
1.7 g fibre

TIPS
I buy flavored tortillas in bulk
and freeze for up to 2 months.
When ready to use,
microwave the package for
30 seconds before pulling out
the number you need.

This wrap has a sweet and sour flavor. Mango chutney can be found in your supermarket, often in the Indian food section. Use good quality steak and be careful not to overcook it.

2 tsp vegetable oil
3/4 cup chopped onions
1/2 cup diced carrots
1 tsp minced garlic
1 tsp curry powder
1-1/4 cups beef or chicken stock
3/4 cup basmati rice
8 oz boneless grilling steak (grill steak while cooking rice)
1/3 cup light sour cream
1/3 cup mango chutney
1/4 cup chopped green onions
1/4 cup chopped fresh coriander or parsley

6 large flour tortillas

1. In a nonstick saucepan, heat oil over medium heat; cook onions, carrots, garlic, and curry for 5 minutes or until onion is browned. Add stock and rice; bring to a boil. Reduce heat to low, cover, and cook for 10 minutes or until rice is tender and liquid is absorbed.
2. Meanwhile, preheat grill or grill pan. Spray with cooking spray. Grill steak over medium-high heat for 8 minutes, turning once, until medium-rare. Transfer to a plate, cover with foil, and set aside until rice is cooked.
3. In a medium bowl, stir together sour cream, chutney, green onions, and coriander.
4. Transfer cooked rice to a bowl. Thinly slice steak; stir into the rice along with the sour cream mixture.
5. Place one-sixth (about 2/3 cup) of warm rice mixture in centre of a tortilla. Roll bottom of tortilla up and over filling tightly, fold in both sides, and continue to roll. Cut in half. Repeat with remaining tortillas and rice mixture. Serve warm.

salads

vegetable crouton salad

PREP: About 20 mins.
COOK: About 10 mins.

MAKES 6 SERVINGS

MAKE AHEAD
Toast bread cubes several days before and keep in an airtight container. Prepare dressing up to 5 days in advance and keep refrigerated.

NUTRITIONAL ANALYSIS PER SERVING
170.4 calories
4.9 g protein
8 g fat, total
1.9 g fat, saturated
19.7 g carbohydrates
320 mg sodium
3.6 mg cholesterol
2.7 g fibre

TIP
Don't toss this salad until you're ready to serve it or the croutons will lose their crunchy texture. Add your favorite dried spice to the bread cubes for extra flavor.

This salad is similar to an Italian bread salad: the difference is that in this recipe the bread is toasted first. Using bread that's a few days old is best. If you choose to use field tomatoes instead of plum, be sure to seed them to get rid of excess juice.

CROUTONS
3 cups 1-inch Italian bread cubes

SALAD
2-1/2 cups chopped plum tomatoes
1-1/2 cups chopped English cucumber, unpeeled
1 cup diced sweet red, green, or yellow peppers
1/2 cup thinly sliced sweet onions
1/4 cup sliced black olives
2 oz light feta cheese, crumbled
1/4 cup chopped fresh parsley

DRESSING
2 tbsp olive oil
1 tbsp fresh lemon juice
1 tbsp balsamic vinegar
1 tsp minced garlic
1 tsp dried oregano
1 tsp granulated sugar
1/2 tsp Dijon mustard
Pinch coarsely ground pepper

1. Preheat oven to 400°F.
2. To make croutons: Place bread cubes on a baking sheet. Spray with cooking spray. Bake for 8 to 10 minutes or until golden, turning once. Set aside.
3. To make salad: In a large bowl, combine salad ingredients.
4. To make dressing: In a small bowl, whisk together dressing ingredients. Pour over salad; toss to coat. Serve garnished with croutons.

portobello mushroom, baby spinach, and parmesan stacked salad

My family and I were in a wonderful restaurant—Blanchard's—on Anguilla, an island in the Caribbean, and had this creative and delicious salad. I came up with my own version and now can't stop serving it.

DRESSING
5 tsp olive oil
1 tbsp balsamic vinegar
1 tsp minced garlic
1/2 tsp Dijon mustard

SALAD
4 portobello mushroom caps
8 cups well-packed baby spinach, washed and dried
1/4 cup freshly grated Parmesan cheese

GARNISH
3 tbsp chopped fresh parsley

1. To make dressing: In a small bowl, mix dressing ingredients until smooth.
2. To make salad: Either on a barbecue or in a nonstick grill pan sprayed with cooking spray, grill mushrooms on medium heat for about 10 to 12 minutes, turning halfway, or until tender. (Spray mushrooms with vegetable spray if they look dry.) Set aside.
3. Meanwhile, in a large nonstick frying pan sprayed with cooking spray, cook spinach on medium heat for 2 minutes just until barely wilted. Divide among 4 serving plates. Pour half of dressing over spinach; sprinkle on half of Parmesan cheese. Place a mushroom cap on top; pour remaining dressing over mushroom; sprinkle on remaining Parmesan. Garnish with parsley.

PREP: About 10 mins.
COOK: About 12 mins.

MAKES 4 SERVINGS

MAKE AHEAD
Prepare dressing up to 3 days in advance. Grill mushrooms up to 1 day in advance. Serve them at room temperature.

NUTRITIONAL ANALYSIS
PER SERVING
98 calories
6.2 g protein
8 g fat, total
1.8 g fat, saturated
5.7 g carbohydrates
224 mg sodium
4.9 mg cholesterol
1.3 g fibre

TIPS
Avoid washing or submerging mushrooms in water. The best way to clean them is to wipe them gently with a wet paper towel. If you prefer, you can slice the mushrooms after they are cooked rather than serving them whole.

PREP: About 15 mins.

MAKES 6 SERVINGS

MAKE AHEAD
Prepare tomatoes early in the
day. Prepare dressing up to
3 days in advance. Dress
salad just before serving.

NUTRITIONAL ANALYSIS
PER SERVING
135 calories
3 g protein
4 g fat, total
0.8 g fat, saturated
18 g carbohydrates
130 mg sodium
0 mg cholesterol
5.2 g fibre

TIPS
You can prepare this salad
early in the day, but don't
chop the basil or pour the
dressing over the salad until
ready to serve. Rather than
buying sun-dried tomatoes
packed in oil, buy dried sun-
dried tomatoes.

four tomato salad

The contrasting colors and textures of the different tomatoes in this salad are what make it so sensational. If you can find grape tomatoes, they are even sweeter than cherry tomatoes and have a great texture. Don't forget that tomatoes contain lycopene, an antioxidant that helps in the fight against prostate cancer and heart disease.

SALAD
1/2 cup sun-dried tomatoes
2 cups sliced field tomatoes
2 cups halved red or yellow cherry tomatoes
2 cups quartered plum tomatoes
1 cup sliced sweet onions such as Vidalia, Walla Walla, or Spanish
1/2 cup chopped fresh basil (or 2 tsp dried basil)

DRESSING
3 tbsp balsamic vinegar
2 tbsp olive oil
1-1/2 tsp minced garlic
1/2 tsp granulated sugar
1/8 tsp freshly ground black pepper

1. Pour boiling water over sun-dried tomatoes to cover. Let stand 15 minutes or until softened. Drain and slice. Alternatively, cover the sun-dried tomatoes with a little water and microwave on High for 1 minute.
2. To make salad: Place tomatoes, onions, and, if using, fresh basil in a serving bowl or on a platter.
3. To make dressing: In a bowl, whisk together vinegar, olive oil, garlic, sugar, pepper, and, if using, dried basil. Pour over salad.

tomato and onion salad with feta cheese dressing

In season, nothing is more delicious than fresh juicy tomatoes and sweet onions with a light feta dressing. Sometimes I'll toss in some cooked chicken or seafood to make this salad a complete meal.

SALAD
2 large field tomatoes, sliced
1/2 medium sweet onion, sliced
1/4 cup sliced black olives

DRESSING
1 oz light feta cheese, crumbled
1-1/2 tbsp light sour cream
1-1/2 tbsp water
1 tbsp light mayonnaise
2 tsp fresh lemon juice
1 tsp dried oregano
1/2 tsp minced garlic
1/4 tsp freshly ground black pepper

GARNISH
2 tbsp chopped fresh parsley or basil

1. To make salad: Arrange tomatoes on a serving platter. Scatter onion and olives over tomatoes.
2. To make dressing: In a food processor, combine dressing ingredients, process until smooth. Drizzle dressing over salad. Garnish with parsley.

PREP: About 15 mins.

MAKES 4 SERVINGS

MAKE AHEAD
Prepare dressing up to 2 days in advance. Don't pour over salad until ready to serve.

NUTRITIONAL ANALYSIS
PER SERVING
85 calories
2.8 g protein
4.7 g fat, total
1.3 g fat, saturated
7.8 g carbohydrates
374 mg sodium
12.4 mg cholesterol
7.4 g fibre

TIPS
Light varieties of feta cheese are now available. Both feta and goat cheeses are lower in fat than regular cheeses and have an intense flavor, which means you don't have to use as much.

avocado, tomato, and onion salad with lime–honey mustard dressing

Avocados, though higher in fat and calories than other fruits or vegetables, are considered a heart-healthy food because they help lower the amount of bad cholesterol in your blood. Enjoy them in moderation.

SALAD

4 cups torn mixed salad greens

1/4 ripe avocado, thinly sliced

3 ripe plum tomatoes, thinly sliced

1/2 cup thinly sliced sweet onion

1/4 cup chopped fresh coriander

DRESSING

2 tbsp fresh lime or lemon juice

1 tbsp olive oil

1-1/2 tsp liquid honey

1/2 tsp Dijon mustard

1/2 tsp minced garlic

1. To make salad: In a large serving bowl, toss together salad ingredients.
2. To make dressing: In a small bowl, whisk together dressing ingredients. Pour over salad; toss to coat.

PREP: About 15 mins.

MAKES 4 SERVINGS

MAKE AHEAD
Dressing can be prepared up to 3 days ahead. If need be, prepare the salad early in the day, but never slice the avocado until ready to serve.

NUTRITIONAL ANALYSIS
PER SERVING
98.4 calories
2 g protein
5.6 g fat, total
0.9 g fat, saturated
10 g carbohydrates
68 mg sodium
0 mg cholesterol
3.2 g fibre

TIPS
Coriander is also known as cilantro or Chinese parsley. It has a very distinctive taste, and you either love it or you don't. If it's not your cup of tea, replace it with parsley, dill, or basil.

spinach and mango salad with black bean dressing

The combination of baby spinach, mango, and black beans is delicious and well balanced. Be sure to choose a ripe mango. I love the Indonesian varieties, which tend to be sweeter than other kinds. If your mango is not as ripe as desired, add a little more honey to the dressing.

SALAD

6 cups baby spinach

1/2 cup sliced sweet red peppers

1/2 cup sliced sweet onions

1/2 cup diced mango

DRESSING

2 tbsp orange juice concentrate, thawed

2 tbsp liquid honey

1 tbsp black bean sauce

2 tsp vegetable oil

2 tsp rice vinegar

1 tsp crushed garlic

1 tsp chopped gingerroot

1 tsp sesame oil

1. To make salad: In a serving bowl, combine all salad ingredients.
2. To make dressing: In a small bowl, combine dressing ingredients, mixing until smooth. Pour dressing over salad; toss to coat.

super quick

PREP: About 15 mins.

MAKES 4 SERVINGS

MAKE AHEAD
Prepare dressing up to 3 days in advance and keep refrigerated. Dress salad just before serving.

NUTRITIONAL ANALYSIS PER SERVING
124 calories
2.1 g protein
3.9 g fat, total
0.4 g fat, saturated
20.2 g carbohydrates
65 mg sodium
0 mg cholesterol
2.4 g fibre

TIPS
Sweet onion varieties include Vadalia, Walla Walla, and Maui. The larger and sweeter the onion, the less you will tear when cutting it.

PREP: About 15 mins.
COOK: About 10 mins.

MAKES 6 SERVINGS

MAKE AHEAD
Prepare this salad up to 1 day
in advance and let it come to
room temperature before
serving.

NUTRITIONAL ANALYSIS
PER SERVING
250 calories
6.1 g protein
5.1 g fat, total
0.6 g fat, saturated
55.5 g carbohydrates
358 mg sodium
0 mg cholesterol
6.34 g fibre

TIP
Serve this salad in a large red
or green cabbage leaf for a
more elegant presentation.

tomato potato salad

The inspiration for this recipe came from one of Toronto's oldest restaurants, the Senator Dining Room. The salad I had there was delicious but had a fair amount of oil. I adapted the idea, using lots of tomatoes for extra moisture and a light Asian dressing. The key to having the potatoes absorb the dressing is to pour it over them when they are still warm.

SALAD
12 small red potatoes (about 1 lb)
4 whole drained canned hearts of palm
3 plum tomatoes, sliced
3/4 cup chopped sweet onions
1/4 cup chopped green onions

DRESSING
2 tbsp rice wine vinegar
2 tbsp low-sodium soy sauce
1 tbsp sesame oil
1 tbsp liquid honey
1 tbsp vegetable oil
1 tsp minced garlic
1 tsp minced gingerroot

GARNISH
1/4 cup chopped fresh coriander or parsley

1. To make salad: Scrub potatoes but do not peel. Cut into quarters. Boil until just tender, approximately 10 to 15 minutes. Drain and place in a serving bowl still hot.
2. To make dressing: In a small bowl, whisk together dressing ingredients. Pour over warm potatoes and toss to coat.
3. Combine remaining salad ingredients with potatoes. Garnish with coriander.

barley, sun-dried tomato pesto, and feta salad

Barley, a great grain, usually is used only in soups, but I love to serve it in a salad. Rather than using pot barley, I tend to use pearl barley because it cooks in less time. Pot barley, however, is less refined than, and therefore more nutritious than, pearl barley.

SALAD
3-1/2 cups vegetable or chicken stock
1 cup pearl barley
2 oz light feta cheese, crumbled
1/4 cup sliced black olives
2 tbsp pine nuts
1/4 cup chopped fresh basil or parsley

SUN-DRIED TOMATO PESTO
1/3 cup chopped rehydrated sun-dried tomatoes
3 tbsp chopped fresh basil or parsley
2 tbsp grated Parmesan cheese
1-1/2 tbsp toasted pine nuts
1/2 tsp minced garlic
1/4 cup vegetable or chicken stock
2 tbsp olive oil

1. To make salad: In a saucepan, bring stock to a boil. Add barley. Reduce heat to low, cover, and cook for 40 minutes or until barley is just tender. Drain any excess liquid. Transfer to large bowl. Cool.
2. To make pesto: In a small food processor, process sun-dried tomatoes, basil, Parmesan, toasted pine nuts, and garlic until finely chopped. With machine running, add stock and olive oil through the feed tube, processing until smooth.
3. Stir pesto and remaining salad ingredients into cooled barley.

PREP: About 10 mins.
COOK: About 40 mins.

MAKES 6 SERVINGS

MAKE AHEAD
Prepare barley salad up to
1 day before serving.

NUTRITIONAL ANALYSIS
PER SERVING
230 calories
10.4 g protein
10.6 g fat, total
2.9 g fat, saturated
30.9 g carbohydrates
288 mg sodium
7.4 mg cholesterol
6.3 g fibre

TIPS
Sun-dried tomato pesto is
great to make in larger quantities and freeze in small containers. It is delicious over
pasta or cooked fish or
chicken. Purchase sun-dried
tomatoes from a bulk food
store and freeze to keep them
fresh. To prepare the sun-
dried tomatoes, just soak
them in boiling water for
15 minutes until soft, or cover
them with a little water and
microwave on High for
1 minute.

barley niçoise salad

Barley is a source of protein, fibre, and iron. After you try this version of Niçoise salad, you may never go back to the traditional version.

PREP: About 15 mins.
COOK: About 30 mins.

MAKES 6 SERVINGS

MAKE AHEAD
Prepare salad and dressing up to 1 day before serving. Barley can be cooked up to 2 days in advance and kept refrigerated (serve at room temperature).

NUTRITIONAL ANALYSIS PER SERVING
246 calories
13 g protein
7.3 g fat, total
1 g fat, saturated
32 g carbohydrates
629 mg sodium
8.3 mg cholesterol
6.6 g fibre

TIPS
When buying canned tuna, select white tuna packed in water, not oil. Compared to water-packed tuna, oil-packed tuna has double the calories and six times the fat.

SALAD
3 cups chicken or vegetable stock
1 cup pearl barley
1 cup sliced green beans
1 cup diced plum tomatoes
1 cup diced English cucumber, unpeeled
1 can (170 g) flaked water-packed tuna, drained
4 anchovy fillets, minced
1/4 cup sliced black olives
1/4 cup diced red onions
1/4 cup each chopped fresh dill and parsley

DRESSING
3 tbsp fresh lemon juice
2 tbsp olive oil
1 tbsp balsamic vinegar
1 tsp Dijon mustard
1 tsp minced garlic
1/4 tsp freshly ground black pepper

1. To make salad: In a saucepan, bring stock to a boil. Stir in barley. Reduce heat to medium-low, cover, and cook for 30 to 40 minutes or until tender. Drain any excess liquid. Transfer to large bowl. Cool to room temperature, or place in refrigerator to cool more quickly.

2. In a pot of boiling water, cook beans for 2 minutes or until tender-crisp. Drain and rinse with cold water. Stir into barley, along with remaining salad ingredients.

3. To make dressing: In a small bowl, whisk together dressing ingredients. Pour over barley mixture; toss to coat.

quinoa with fennel, red pepper, and apricots in an orange dressing

 quick

Quinoa is such a versatile healthy grain and the only one considered a complete protein. The fennel, sweet peppers, apricots, dried cranberries, and orange dressing give this salad a sweet flavor. It goes beautifully with fish or chicken and is a great dish to serve in a buffet meal.

SALAD

2 cups vegetable or chicken stock

1 cup quinoa, rinsed and drained

1 cup diced fennel

1 cup diced sweet red peppers

1 cup diced snow peas

1/2 cup diced dried apricots

1/4 cup dried cranberries or dried cherries or raisins

1/4 cup chopped fresh basil

DRESSING

2 tbsp raspberry vinegar

2 tbsp orange juice concentrate, thawed

1 tbsp liquid honey

1 tbsp olive oil

1 tsp minced garlic

1. To make salad: In a saucepan, bring stock to a boil. Add quinoa; reduce heat to medium-low. Cook, covered, for 15 minutes or until tender and liquid is absorbed. Transfer to a bowl. Cool.
2. Stir remaining salad ingredients into cooled quinoa.
3. To make dressing: In a small bowl, whisk together dressing ingredients. Pour over quinoa mixture; toss to coat.

PREP: About 10 mins.
COOK: About 15 mins.

MAKES 6 SERVINGS

MAKE AHEAD
Prepare quinoa up to 1 day in advance. Dressing can be prepared up to 3 days before serving. Toss salad with dressing and refrigerate for up to 2 days.

NUTRITIONAL ANALYSIS PER SERVING
220 calories
6 g protein
4.5 g fat, total
0.7 g fat, saturated
42 g carbohydrates
106 mg sodium
1.2 mg cholesterol
4.8 g fibre

TIPS
I purchase my dried fruits in bulk and keep them in the freezer. Try cutting apricots or other dried fruit with scissors sprayed with cooking spray to prevent sticking.

PREP: About 15 mins.
COOK: About 10 mins.

MAKES 6 SERVINGS

MAKE AHEAD
Sauté corn up to 1 day in
advance. Prepare salad earlier
in the day and refrigerate to
allow to marinate in the
dressing.

NUTRITIONAL ANALYSIS
PER SERVING
162 calories
4 g protein
2.6 g fat, total
0.4 g fat, saturated
30 g carbohydrates
184 mg sodium
0 mg cholesterol
4.6 g fibre

TIPS
I often have a hard time finding a ripe mango. Unripe
mangoes are not sweet, have
too firm a texture, and take
some of the great taste away
from this salad. I have found
that Indonesian mangoes,
which are smaller than other
varieties, are always sweeter.
Sautéing the corn gives a
charred texture and sweet
taste.

roasted corn black bean salad

This salad of contrasting colors is not only beautiful, but also delicious. Serve it in a lettuce, Belgian endive, or cabbage leaf. It can also be used as a salsa over fish or chicken.

SALAD
2 cups drained canned corn
1/2 cup chopped sweet onions
1 tsp minced garlic
1-1/2 cups diced mango
1 cup rinsed and drained canned black beans
3/4 cup chopped sweet red or yellow peppers
Lettuce leaves

DRESSING
1/3 cup chopped fresh coriander
3 tbsp fresh lemon juice
2 tbsp orange juice concentrate, thawed
1 tbsp olive oil
1 tsp minced garlic
1/4 to 1/2 tsp hot pepper sauce

1. In a nonstick skillet sprayed with cooking spray and set over medium heat, cook corn for 8 minutes, stirring often, or until slightly charred. Stir in onions and garlic; cook for 2 minutes longer. Transfer to a bowl; cool.
2. To make dressing: In a small bowl, whisk together dressing ingredients.
3. To make salad: Stir mango, beans, and peppers into cooled corn mixture. Pour dressing over; toss to coat. Serve on lettuce leaves.

chick-pea salad with tahini dressing

I love hummus, and when I separated the foods in this Middle Eastern dish, I discovered that they could make a delicious and interesting salad. It's a filling and satisfying main dish salad.

SALAD

2 cups rinsed and drained canned chick-peas

1-1/2 cups chopped sweet green peppers

1-1/2 cups chopped carrots

1/2 cup chopped celery

1/2 cup chopped green onions

DRESSING

1/3 cup smooth 5% ricotta cheese

3 tbsp water

2 tbsp tahini (sesame seed paste)

2 tbsp light mayonnaise

2 tbsp fresh lemon juice

2 tbsp olive oil

1-1/2 tbsp soy sauce

1 tsp crushed garlic

1/4 tsp cumin (optional)

1/3 cup chopped fresh coriander or parsley

1. To make salad: In a bowl, combine all salad ingredients.
2. To make dressing: In a food processor or blender, process all dressing ingredients, except coriander, until smooth. Combine with salad and coriander; toss to coat.

PREP: About 15 mins.

MAKES 6 SERVINGS

MAKE AHEAD
Prepare salad up to 1 day in advance. Prepare dressing up to 2 days in advance and keep refrigerated.

NUTRITIONAL ANALYSIS PER SERVING
226 calories
6 g protein
10 g fat, total
2 g fat, saturated
23 g carbohydrates
400 mg sodium
6 mg cholesterol
6 g fibre

TIPS
Instead of using canned chick-peas, cook dried ones. They don't need to be soaked overnight. Just cook them in boiling water for 3 minutes. Leave covered for 1 hour, drain water, cover with fresh water, and simmer for 20 to 30 minutes or just until tender.

bulgur shrimp salad

Bulgur is often used in the traditional dish tabbouleh, but here's another great way to use this versatile and healthy grain. Be sure to cook bulgur on low heat to prevent scorching the pan.

2 cups vegetable or chicken stock
1 cup bulgur
12 oz deveined peeled shrimp
1 cup drained canned corn
2/3 cup chopped plum tomatoes
1/2 cup diced roasted peppers
1-1/2 oz light feta cheese, crumbled
1/3 cup chopped fresh dill or parsley
1/3 cup diced green onions
1/4 cup fresh lemon juice
2 tbsp olive oil
1-1/2 tsp minced garlic
1/4 tsp each salt and pepper

1. Spray a small pot with cooking spray. Add stock and bulgur; bring to a boil. Reduce heat to low, cover, and cook for 12 minutes or until stock is absorbed and bulgur is soft. Place in a serving bowl. Cool to room temperature.
2. In a nonstick skillet sprayed with cooking spray, cook shrimp over medium heat for 5 minutes just until cooked. Remove from pan, dice, and place in the serving bowl with the bulgur. Respray pan and cook corn over medium-high heat for 5 minutes or until slightly blackened. Add to shrimp-bulgur mixture.
3. Stir in remaining ingredients.

PREP: About 15 mins.
COOK: About 22 mins.

MAKES 6 SERVINGS

MAKE AHEAD
Prepare salad 1 day before serving (keep refrigerated). Bulgur can be prepared in advance and kept for up to 2 days if refrigerated.

NUTRITIONAL ANALYSIS PER SERVING
256 calories
17.8 g protein
7.5 g fat, total
1.9 g fat, saturated
29.3 g carbohydrates
427 mg sodium
92.5 mg cholesterol
5.6 g fibre

TIPS
You could omit the shrimp to make the dish vegetarian, or replace the shrimp with chicken, tofu, or other seafood. Substitute quinoa, millet, or wheatberries for the bulgur. The latter take more than 40 minutes to cook.

lettuce, shrimp, and couscous salad

This version of a couscous lettuce salad has an Asian flavor. The combination of couscous, shrimp, and sweet peppers goes so well with the sesame dressing. Don't pour the dressing over the salad until ready to serve or the lettuce will wilt.

SALAD

1 cup chicken or vegetable stock

1 cup couscous

2 cups thinly sliced romaine lettuce

1/2 cup diced sweet red peppers

1/3 cup chopped fresh basil, coriander, or parsley

8 oz cooked deveined peeled shrimp, diced

DRESSING

1-1/2 tbsp rice wine vinegar

2 tbsp low-sodium soy sauce

5 tsp liquid honey

2 tsp sesame oil

1-1/2 tsp minced garlic

1/4 to 1/2 tsp hot pepper sauce

1/8 tsp each salt and freshly ground black pepper

1. To make salad: In a small saucepan, bring stock to a boil. Remove from heat. Stir in couscous, cover, and let stand for 5 minutes. Fluff with a fork. Transfer to a large bowl. Cool.

2. Stir remaining salad ingredients into cooled couscous.

3. To make dressing: In a small bowl, whisk together dressing ingredients. Pour over couscous mixture; toss to coat.

PREP: About 10 mins.
COOK: About 5 mins.

MAKES 6 SERVINGS

MAKE AHEAD
Couscous can be prepared up to 1 day in advance, but keep it covered in the refrigerator. Dressing can be prepared up to 4 days in advance. The tossed salad can be kept refrigerated for up to 2 days.

NUTRITIONAL ANALYSIS PER SERVING
189.1 calories
12.6 g protein
2.7 g fat, total
0.5 g fat, saturated
28.6 g carbohydrates
223 mg sodium
58.1 mg cholesterol
2.2 g fibre

TIPS
You can substitute cooked chicken, beef, or beans for the shrimp. For a firmer texture, try using nappa cabbage instead of the romaine.

southwest shrimp salad in egg roll cups

PREP: About 15 mins.
COOK: About 15 mins.

MAKES 12 SERVINGS

MAKE AHEAD
Bake egg rolls up to 2 weeks in advance and keep in an air-tight container. Dressing can be prepared up to 2 days in advance if refrigerated. Prepare salad early in the day, but don't put it in the baked egg roll cups until ready to serve.

NUTRITIONAL ANALYSIS PER SERVING
171 calories
11.6 g protein
2.7 g fat, total
0.4 g fat, saturated
25 g carbohydrates
371 mg sodium
61.7 mg cholesterol
1.3 g fibre

TIP
Weigh the shrimp after they have been peeled and deveined.

I did this salad on Marilyn Dennis's *City Line* show, and the e-mails came in for two days! The egg roll cups are delicious and not deep-fried like similar cups served in Mexican restaurants. If desired, serve the salad in a large bowl.

SALAD
12 large (5-1/2 inch) egg roll wrappers (prepare salad while baking egg roll cups)
1 lb deveined peeled shrimp
1 tsp minced garlic
1 cup drained canned corn
1-1/2 cups chopped plum tomatoes
1/2 cup chopped sweet red peppers
1/3 cup chopped fresh coriander or parsley

DRESSING
1/4 cup barbecue sauce
3 tbsp light mayonnaise
1 tbsp molasses
1/2 tsp hot sauce
1/8 tsp each salt and pepper

GARNISH
3 tbsp chopped fresh coriander

1. Preheat oven to 425°F. Spray 12-cup muffin tin with cooking spray.
2. Fit egg roll wrappers into muffin cups. Bake for 8 minutes or just until browned. Set aside.
3. To make salad: Meanwhile, in a nonstick skillet sprayed with cooking spray, cook shrimp and garlic over medium-high heat just until cooked, about 5 minutes. Chop and place in a bowl. Respray pan; cook corn over medium-high heat for 8 minutes or just until browned. Add to shrimp. Cool. Add remaining salad ingredients.
4. To make dressing: In a small bowl, mix dressing ingredients until smooth. Pour over salad and toss well. Divide salad evenly among egg roll cups. Garnish with coriander.

sushi salad

You can't keep me away from sushi. I could eat it daily. For this recipe, I turned the main ingredients of a California roll into a very special salad. My friends rate this as my number one salad, and it's a lot less expensive than sushi!

SALAD
1-1/2 cups sushi rice
1-1/2 cups water
1/4 cup rice wine vinegar
1 tbsp granulated sugar
6 oz crabmeat or surimi (imitation crab), diced
1 cup diced cucumbers
1/2 cup diced carrots
1/2 cup diced sweet red peppers
1/3 cup diced green onions
1/2 cup diced avocado
1/2 sheet nori (seaweed), cut into thin strips

DRESSING
1/4 cup light mayonnaise
1/4 cup light sour cream
1/2 tsp wasabi (Japanese horseradish) paste
4 tsp soy sauce
1 tsp toasted sesame seeds

1. To make salad: Bring rice and water to a boil. Reduce heat to low, cover, and cook for 12 minutes. Remove pan from heat. Let stand covered for 10 minutes. While rice is hot, add rice wine vinegar and sugar; stir until well mixed. Place rice mixture in a serving bowl. Cool until rice is still warm but not hot.
2. Stir in remaining salad ingredients, except avocado and nori.
3. To make dressing: In a small bowl, whisk together all dressing ingredients; pour over rice mixture and toss to coat. Add avocado and nori and toss gently.

PREP: About 15 mins.
COOK: About 12 mins.

MAKES 6 SERVINGS

MAKE AHEAD
Prepare salad up to 1 day in advance.

NUTRITIONAL ANALYSIS PER SERVING
145 calories
8.2 g protein
6.1 g fat, total
1.5 g fat, saturated
14.3 g carbohydrates
327 mg sodium
26.9 mg cholesterol
1.9 g fibre

TIPS
To keep cooked sushi rice fresh for a few hours, place it on a baking sheet and cover with a wet towel. You can also keep it airtight in a large baggie. These tips work only on the day the rice is cooked. Toast sesame seeds in a small skillet on high for 1 to 2 minutes or until lightly browned.

PREP: About 10 mins.
COOK: About 5 mins.

MAKES 4 SERVINGS

MAKE AHEAD
Prepare dressing up to 4 days
in advance and keep refrigerated. If serving cold or at
room temperature, grill tuna
early in day. Do not reheat.

NUTRITIONAL ANALYSIS
PER SERVING
163 calories
21 g protein
2.9 g fat, total
0.6 g fat, saturated
13.3 g carbohydrates
467 mg sodium
40 mg cholesterol
3.2 g fibre

TIP
When I purchase fresh tuna,
I always go to a reputable
fish market and ask for sushi-
quality tuna.

fresh tuna salad

Forget canned tuna and try fresh tuna steak to make the best salad you'll ever have. The key is to not overcook the tuna, which makes it dry. It's best just to sear the outside of the tuna and take it off the heat. For some people, this might be a little too rare, so cook it another minute or two, but no more!

SALAD
12 oz fresh tuna steak
6 cups chopped leafy lettuce
1 cup sliced cherry tomatoes
1/3 cup diced red onions
1/3 cup sliced black olives

DRESSING
2 tbsp soy sauce
1 tbsp rice vinegar
1 tbsp honey
2 tsp sesame oil
2 tsp toasted sesame seeds
1/2 tsp minced garlic
1/2 tsp minced gingerroot

GARNISH
3 tbsp chopped fresh coriander or parsley

1. In a nonstick skillet or grill pan sprayed with cooking spray, cook tuna over medium-high heat for about 5 minutes, turning once, or until medium rare (or to your liking). Set aside.
2. To make salad: In a serving bowl, toss lettuce, tomatoes, onions, and olives.
3. To make dressing: In a small bowl, combine dressing ingredients, reserving 1 tsp sesame seeds.
4. Slice tuna thinly; place over top of salad. Pour dressing over; toss gently. Sprinkle with coriander and remaining sesame seeds.

mussel salad with roasted peppers, goat cheese, and basil

This salad is so easy and yet so sophisticated. It's great for a dinner party or a weekend brunch. Leftovers can be served the next day.

1 large sweet red pepper

1/2 cup white wine, fish stock, or water

2 lb mussels

1/3 cup diced red onions

2 tbsp toasted pine nuts

2 tsp olive oil

1 tsp minced garlic

1/4 tsp ground pepper

1 oz goat cheese, crumbled

GARNISH

1/4 cup chopped fresh basil

1. Grill or broil pepper over medium-high heat until charred, about 15 to 20 minutes. (If broiling, place pepper in middle of oven so as not to burn it.) Cool, remove skin and seeds, and dice. Set aside.

2. In a large saucepan, bring wine to a boil. Add mussels, cover, and cook for 5 minutes or until mussels open. Discard any that do not open. Drain; set aside until cool. Shell mussels; place in a serving bowl.

3. Stir in remaining salad ingredients; toss until combined. Garnish with basil.

PREP: About 10 mins.
COOK: About 20 mins.

MAKES 6 SERVINGS

MAKE AHEAD
Prepare entire salad early in day and refrigerate to marinate.

NUTRITIONAL ANALYSIS PER SERVING
192 calories
20 g protein
7.4 g fat, total
1.8 g fat, saturated
8.2 g carbohydrates
503 mg sodium
45 mg cholesterol
0.6 g fibre

TIPS
If you don't feel like roasting your own peppers, you can use bottled roasted peppers that are packed in water. Use about 3 to 4 ounces, which equals 1 large pepper.

PREP: About 15 mins.
COOK: About 8 mins.

MAKES 6 SERVINGS

MAKE AHEAD
Prepare bread cubes up to
2 weeks in advance and keep
in an airtight container.
Dressing can be made up to
2 days in advance if
refrigerated.

NUTRITIONAL ANALYSIS
PER SERVING
199 calories
12.8 g protein
10 g fat, total
4 g fat, saturated
10.5 g carbohydrates
666 mg sodium
62 mg cholesterol
1.9 g fibre

TIPS
I often buy extra smoked
trout, vacuum packed, when
it's on sale and freeze it. It's a
great substitute for smoked
salmon when you want a
change.

smoked trout caesar salad with goat cheese and croutons

At a Muskoka resort in Bracebridge, Ontario, I always order this great green salad containing smoked trout. I decided to alter the salad by dressing it with a Caesar dressing and adding goat cheese and some large homemade croutons. It's sensational.

CROUTONS
2 cups 1-inch cubes Italian bread

SALAD
4 oz smoked trout, crumbled
2 oz goat cheese, crumbled
8 cups torn romaine lettuce

DRESSING
1 egg
3 tbsp grated Parmesan cheese
3 thin anchovy fillets, minced
1 tbsp fresh lemon juice
1 tsp Dijon mustard
1-1/2 tsp minced garlic
1/8 tsp ground pepper
2 tbsp olive oil

1. To make croutons: Preheat oven to 425°F. Place bread cubes on a baking sheet; spray them with vegetable oil. Bake for 8 to 10 minutes or until golden.
2. To make salad: Place trout, cheese, and lettuce in a large salad bowl along with croutons.
3. To make dressing: Combine all dressing ingredients in a small food processor or whisk together in a bowl until smooth. Pour over salad and toss to coat.

chicken and greens with sesame dressing

Tahini, a sesame seed paste or butter, is traditionally used in Middle Eastern cooking. You've probably had it with falafels. If you don't have tahini, substitute any other nut butter. The dressing can be used on other salads or as a condiment for sandwiches.

8 oz boneless skinless chicken breast (about 2 breasts)

DRESSING
2 tbsp tahini
3 tbsp water
2 tbsp honey
1 tbsp low-sodium soy sauce
1 tbsp oyster or hoisin sauce
2 tsp sesame oil
1 tsp minced garlic

SALAD
6 cups torn mixed salad greens
1 sweet red pepper, thinly sliced
1 cup sliced snow peas
1/4 cup chopped green onions
1/4 cup chopped fresh coriander

GARNISH
2 tsp toasted sesame seeds

1. Preheat barbecue. On a grill sprayed with cooking spray, cook chicken over medium-high heat for 6 minutes per side or until cooked through. (Alternatively, cook in a nonstick grill pan sprayed with cooking spray over medium-high heat for 12 minutes, turning once, or until cooked through.) Slice thinly.
2. To make dressing: In a small bowl, whisk together dressing ingredients until smooth.
3. To make salad: In a large bowl, combine salad ingredients. Pour dressing over; toss to coat. Place chicken on top. Sprinkle with sesame seeds before serving.

PREP: About 15 mins.
COOK: About 12 mins.

MAKES 6 SERVINGS

MAKE AHEAD
Prepare dressing up to 3 days in advance. Toss with salad just before serving.

NUTRITIONAL ANALYSIS PER SERVING
143 calories
12.2 g protein
5.4 g fat, total
0.8 g fat, saturated
11.5 g carbohydrates
152 mg sodium
24.2 mg cholesterol
2.4 g fibre

TIPS
To toast sesame seeds, place in a skillet over medium-high heat and toast for 2 to 3 minutes or just until seeds begin to brown. You can buy packaged pre-washed mixed salad greens, also called mesclun, in the produce section of many supermarkets.

new-style cobb salad

PREP: About 15 mins.
COOK: About 12 mins.

MAKES 6 SERVINGS

MAKE AHEAD
Prepare the salad up to 3
days in advance. Dress it just
before serving.

NUTRITIONAL ANALYSIS
PER SERVING
111.2 calories
6.5 g protein
6.4 g fat, total
1.5 g fat, saturated
6.9 g carbohydrates
129 mg sodium
13.8 mg cholesterol
2.9 g fibre

TIP
To prevent avocado from turning brown, before cutting the
avocado and without piercing
it, microwave on High for
30 seconds. It truly works!

A cobb salad usually is loaded with calories and fat from the excess cheese, eggs, avocado, and bacon. In this delicious version, I use lean chicken breast, a quarter of an avocado, and only a small amount of blue cheese to make the dressing. It's outstanding.

SALAD
4 oz boneless skinless chicken breast (about 1 breast)
4 cups torn mixed salad greens
1-1/2 cups diced plum tomatoes
1/3 cup chopped green onions
1/4 ripe avocado, chopped
1/4 cup sliced black olives

DRESSING
1-1/2 oz blue cheese, crumbled
2 tbsp fresh lemon juice
1-1/2 tbsp light sour cream
1-1/2 tbsp olive oil
2 tbsp water
1/2 tsp minced garlic

1. To make salad: Preheat barbecue. On grill sprayed with cooking spray, cook chicken over medium-high heat for 6 minutes per side or until cooked through. (Alternatively, cook in a nonstick grill pan sprayed with cooking spray over medium-high heat for 12 minutes, turning once, or until cooked through.) Dice. Arrange chicken and other salad ingredients on a serving platter in rows.
2. To make dressing: In a small bowl or food processor, whisk dressing ingredients until smooth. Drizzle over salad.

chicken salad in lettuce cups

Chicken salad often contains excess calories and fat because of the mayonnaise used in it. In this salad, the calories and fat are reduced by using a variety of diced vegetables, a barbecue sauce–based salad dressing, and only a small amount of light mayonnaise.

SALAD

8 oz boneless skinless chicken breast (about 2 breasts)

1-1/4 cups roughly chopped broccoli

3/4 cup diced carrots

1-1/4 cups diced sweet red peppers

1/2 cup diced sweet onions

1/4 cup finely chopped green onions

1/4 cup chopped fresh dill or parsley

DRESSING

1/4 cup barbecue sauce

3 tbsp light mayonnaise

1 tbsp molasses

1 tsp minced garlic

6 leaves iceberg lettuce or red or green cabbage

1. Preheat barbecue. To make salad: On a grill sprayed with cooking spray, cook chicken over medium-high heat for 6 minutes per side or until cooked through. (Alternatively, cook in a nonstick grill pan over medium-high heat for 12 minutes, turning once, or until cooked through.) Cool. Dice.
2. Steam or boil broccoli and carrots for 3 to 5 minutes or until tender. Rinse with cold water and drain.
3. In a large bowl, stir together all salad ingredients.
4. To make dressing: In a small bowl, whisk together dressing ingredients until smooth. Pour over chicken mixture; toss to coat.
5. Place a lettuce leaf, cupped side up, on each of 6 plates. Divide chicken salad among lettuce cups.

PREP: About 15 mins.
COOK: About 15 mins.

MAKES 6 SERVINGS

MAKE AHEAD
Prepare salad up to 1 day in advance. Prepare dressing up to 3 days in advance. Toss with salad just before serving.

NUTRITIONAL ANALYSIS
PER SERVING
90 calories
10.3 g protein
3.4 g fat, total
0.6 g fat, saturated
11.1 g carbohydrates
184 mg sodium
24.6 mg cholesterol
2.5 g fibre

TIPS
For a beautiful presentation, serve this salad in either a lettuce or cabbage leaf. You can always use leftover chicken or turkey for this recipe. Use a regular flavored, good-quality barbecue sauce.

PREP: About 15 mins.
COOK: About 10 mins.

MAKES 6 SERVINGS

MAKE AHEAD
The entire salad can be made early in the day and refrigerated. Serve at room temperature. The dressing can be made up to 3 days in advance.

NUTRITIONAL ANALYSIS PER SERVING
192 calories
13.3 g protein
5 g fat, total
0.7 g fat, saturated
23.4 g carbohydrates
326 mg sodium
22.1 mg cholesterol
2.3 g fibre

TIPS
You can replace the chicken with shrimp, beef, pork, or tofu. The cornstarch keeps the chicken morsels tender.

thai chicken noodle salad

This light side or main dish salad has a wonderful texture and taste. If you can find bean thread or cellophane noodles, they are the best ones to use. Usually a good supermarket has them, or any Asian market.

SALAD
8 oz boneless skinless chicken breast (about 2 breasts), diced
2 tbsp cornstarch
2 tsp vegetable oil
4 oz rice stick noodles (1/4 inch) or bean thread noodles
1 cup thinly sliced sweet red peppers
1/2 cup thinly sliced carrots
1/3 cup chopped green onions
1/3 cup chopped fresh coriander or parsley
3 tbsp chopped toasted peanuts

DRESSING
2 tbsp hoisin sauce
1 tbsp fresh lemon juice
2 tbsp soy sauce
1-1/2 tsp minced garlic
1 tsp chopped gingerroot
1-1/2 tsp honey
1/2 tsp hot sauce

1. To make salad: Dust chicken with cornstarch. In a nonstick skillet sprayed with cooking spray, heat oil over medium-high heat; cook chicken until cooked though, about 5 minutes. Place in a serving bowl.

2. In a pot of boiling water, cook rice noodles for 5 minutes or just until tender. Drain. Rinse under cold running water; drain. Cut into bite-sized pieces. Add noodles and remaining salad ingredients to chicken.

3. To make dressing: In a small bowl, mix all dressing ingredients until smooth. Pour over salad; toss to coat.

side dishes

PREP: About 10 mins.
COOK: About 5 mins.

MAKES 4 SERVINGS

MAKE AHEAD
Make filling up to 2 days in
advance and the stacks a few
hours before baking.

NUTRITIONAL ANALYSIS
PER SERVING
92 calories
5.2 g protein
4.8 g fat, total
2.4 g fat, saturated
6.9 g carbohydrates
173 mg sodium
8.6 mg cholesterol
1.6 g fibre

TIP
To toast the pine nuts, heat a
small skillet and cook them
on high for about 2 to 3 minutes or until nuts begin to
brown.

sliced tomato stacks

What a way to liven up the basic field tomato! These tomato "sandwiches" are filled with a deli-cious cheese and sun-dried tomato filling topped with toasted pine nuts. Tomatoes are packed with nutrition and contain lycopene, an antioxidant that helps in the fight against prostate cancer.

2 large field tomatoes
1-1/2 oz goat cheese, crumbled
1 oz light cream cheese, softened
1/4 cup chopped rehydrated sun-dried tomatoes
1/2 tsp dried basil
1-1/2 tsp grated Parmesan cheese
1-1/2 tsp toasted pine nuts

1. Preheat oven to 400°F.
2. Slice tomatoes thickly into 4 slices each.
3. In a bowl, stir together goat cheese, cream cheese, sun-dried tomatoes, basil, and half of the Parmesan. Place 4 slices of tomato on a baking sheet. Spread the goat cheese mixture evenly over the slices. Top with remaining slices of tomato. Sprinkle with pine nuts and remaining Parmesan.
4. Bake in the centre of the oven for 5 minutes or until just warmed through.

asian-flavored swiss chard

Swiss chard is an excellent source of beta carotene, which is known to help in the fight against cancer. Remember: the darker green a vegetable is, the healthier for you it is. This vegetable is quite versatile as well as good for you: its ivory stalks can be cooked like asparagus and the dark leaves can be steamed or stir-fried. Or use the stalks and leaves together.

1 lb Swiss chard leaves, coarsely chopped

4 tsp liquid honey

2 tsp rice wine vinegar

2 tsp sesame oil

1 tsp low-sodium soy sauce

1 tsp minced garlic

1/2 tsp minced gingerroot

GARNISH

2 tsp sesame seeds

1. In a nonstick skillet sprayed with cooking spray and set over medium-high heat, cook Swiss chard for 3 to 4 minutes or until wilted.
2. Meanwhile, in a small bowl mix remaining ingredients, except sesame seeds. Add mixture to Swiss chard; cook for 1 minute. Serve sprinkled with sesame seeds.

super
quick

PREP: About 10 mins.
COOK: About 5 mins.

MAKES 4 SERVINGS

MAKE AHEAD
Mix sauce up to 3 days in advance. Cook Swiss chard just before serving.

NUTRITIONAL ANALYSIS
PER SERVING
85 calories
2.5 g protein
3.4 g fat, total
0.5 g fat, saturated
11 g carbohydrates
287 mg sodium
0 mg cholesterol
2.1 g fibre

TIPS
Swiss chard is too bitter to eat raw, but be careful not to overcook it. It tastes best when it is still slightly firm and just a little wilted.

PREP: About 10 mins.
COOK: About 15 mins.

MAKES 4 SERVINGS

MAKE AHEAD
Prepare this dish up to 1 day
in advance. Heat just before
serving.

NUTRITIONAL ANALYSIS
PER SERVING
90 calories
4.3 g protein
6.4 g fat, total
2.2 g fat, saturated
3.8 g carbohydrates
139 mg sodium
6 mg cholesterol
1.3 g fibre

zucchini with pesto, roasted pepper, and goat cheese

Zucchini by itself can lack flavor. When seasoned with pesto, roasted peppers, goat cheese, and pine nuts, it truly comes alive.

1 large zucchini or 2 small, each sliced lengthwise into 4 slices
2 tbsp Rose's Light Pesto (see page 184) or store-bought
1/4 cup chopped drained bottled roasted red peppers (about 2 oz)
1 oz goat cheese, crumbled
1 tbsp chopped toasted pine nuts

1. Preheat oven to 425°F. Spray rimmed baking sheet with cooking spray.
2. Either on a barbecue or in a nonstick grill pan sprayed with cooking spray, cook zucchini over medium heat for about 10 minutes just until tender, turning halfway through cooking.
3. Spread slices with pesto. Sprinkle with peppers, goat cheese, and pine nuts. Bake for 5 minutes.

asparagus with black bean sauce

Asparagus is a wonderful vegetable on its own, but this black bean sauce definitely makes it a highlight.

SAUCE

2 tbsp packed brown sugar

2 tbsp ketchup

1 tbsp black bean sauce

1-1/2 tsp rice wine vinegar

1 tsp sesame oil

1 tsp each minced garlic and gingerroot

1-1/2 lb asparagus, trimmed

GARNISH

1 tsp toasted sesame seeds

1. To make sauce: In a small skillet, whisk together sauce ingredients. Heat gently just until warm, about 1 minute.

2. Either steam or boil asparagus for 3 minutes or just until asparagus turns bright green and is tender-crisp. Drain. Pour sauce over top. Serve sprinkled with sesame seeds.

PREP: About 5 mins.
COOK: About 4 mins.

MAKES 6 SERVINGS

MAKE AHEAD
Prepare sauce up to 1 week in advance. You can increase the amount of sauce you make and freeze for up to 2 months. Cook asparagus early in the day and rinse with cold water. Reheat quickly in boiling water.

NUTRITIONAL ANALYSIS
PER SERVING
66 calories
2.6 g protein
1.3 g fat, total
0.4 g fat, saturated
10 g carbohydrates
90 mg sodium
0 mg cholesterol
2.7 g fibre

TIP
Be sure to use only a small amount of black bean sauce: it can be quite overpowering.

shoestring fries

PREP: About 10 mins.
COOK: About 40 mins.

MAKES 4 SERVINGS

MAKE AHEAD
Slice potatoes and coat with
oil mixture up to a couple of
hours before baking.

NUTRITIONAL ANALYSIS
PER SERVING
115 calories
2.6 g protein
4.1 g fat, total
0.8 g fat, saturated
16.8 g carbohydrates
108 mg sodium
1 mg cholesterol
1.5 g fibre

French fries, usually deep-fried and high in fat, have to be one of the most delicious and addictive foods. These lower-fat fries—which really are "bakes"—are also addictive. (Take a look at them on the front cover.)

2 large baking potatoes (about 1-1/2 lb), unpeeled and scrubbed
1 tbsp olive oil
2 tbsp grated Parmesan cheese
1/8 tsp each salt and freshly ground black pepper
1/8 tsp garlic powder
1/8 tsp chili powder

1. Preheat oven to 425°F. Spray 2 small rimmed baking sheets with cooking spray.
2. Cut potatoes lengthwise in half. Slice each half into 8 wedges. Stack and thinly slice wedges into shoestring shapes about 1/4-inch wide. Place in bowl. Add remaining ingredients and toss well. Spread out on baking sheets.
3. Bake in centre of oven for 40 to 45 minutes, turning fries occasionally, or until browned and crisp.

sweet potato fries with cinnamon and maple syrup

Sweet potatoes are the newest craze. They are more nutritious than regular potatoes and contain antioxidants that may help in the fight against cancer.

2 large sweet potatoes (about 1-1/2 lb), unpeeled and scrubbed
1-1/2 tbsp vegetable oil, melted butter, or margarine
4 tsp maple syrup
3/4 tsp cinnamon
1/4 tsp ground ginger
Pinch nutmeg

1. Preheat oven to 425°F. Spray rimmed baking sheet with cooking spray.
2. Cut sweet potatoes lengthwise in half and each half into 4 wedges. Place on prepared baking sheet. In a small bowl, combine remaining ingredients; brush half of mixture over sweet potatoes.
3. Bake in centre of oven for 20 minutes. Turn and brush with remaining maple syrup mixture. Bake another 15 minutes or until tender.

PREP: About 5 mins.
COOK: About 35 mins.

MAKES 6 SERVINGS

MAKE AHEAD
Cut fries early in the day and cover in water to keep fresh. It's best to bake them just before serving.

NUTRITIONAL ANALYSIS
PER SERVING
160 calories
2.1 g protein
3.5 g fat, total
0.2 g fat, saturated
30 g carbohydrates
12 mg sodium
0 mg cholesterol
3.9 g fibre

yukon gold and sweet potato mash

If you're tired of plain old mashed potatoes, this twist containing sweet potatoes and roasted garlic is a must. The best potato for taste and for mashing is the Yukon Gold, which has a buttery creamy flavor. The sweet potato, with its dark orange pulp, is high in nutrition and antioxidants.

8 large cloves garlic, unpeeled (bake garlic while boiling potatoes)
1 medium Yukon Gold potato (about 8 oz), peeled and cubed
1 medium sweet potato (about 8 oz), peeled and cubed
2 tbsp grated Parmesan cheese
2 tbsp 2% evaporated milk
1 tbsp olive oil
1/4 tsp each salt and freshly ground black pepper

GARNISH
2 tbsp finely chopped fresh parsley

1. Preheat oven or toaster oven to 425°F.
2. Wrap garlic cloves in foil. Bake for 20 minutes or until soft. Meanwhile, place potatoes and sweet potatoes in a saucepan; cover them with cold water. Bring to a boil; cook for 15 to 20 minutes or until tender when pierced with the tip of a sharp knife. Drain.
3. Squeeze garlic from skins; add garlic to potatoes with remaining ingredients. Mash potato mixture until smooth. Serve sprinkled with parsley.

PREP: About 10 mins.
COOK: About 20 mins.

MAKES 4 SERVINGS

MAKE AHEAD
Prepare the day before and heat gently to warm. Can be frozen for up to 1 month.

NUTRITIONAL ANALYSIS
PER SERVING
159 calories
4.6 g protein
4.8 g fat, total
1.2 g fat, saturated
24.3 g carbohydrates
125 mg sodium
3 mg cholesterol
3 g fibre

TIP
If you want to be more organized, cut the potatoes early in the day or the night before and place them in cold water.

garlic mashed potatoes with caramelized onions

Here's another great variation on mashed potatoes: the caramelized onions mixed into the mashed potato and served over top make this dish a winner. I love it served with meat, chicken, or just by itself.

GARLIC MASHED POTATOES

2 medium Yukon Gold potatoes (about 1 lb), peeled and cubed

1/3 cup low-fat sour cream

1 tbsp olive oil

2 tsp minced garlic

1/4 tsp each salt and freshly ground black pepper

CARAMELIZED ONIONS

6 cups sliced sweet onions (about 2 large)

1 tbsp minced garlic

1 tbsp balsamic vinegar

2 tsp packed brown sugar

GARNISH

2 tbsp chopped fresh parsley

1. To make potatoes: Place potatoes in a saucepan; add cold water to cover. Bring to a boil; cook for 15 to 20 minutes or until tender when pierced with the tip of a sharp knife. Drain potatoes; mash. Stir in remaining potato ingredients. Set potatoes aside.

2. To make onions: Meanwhile, in a large nonstick skillet sprayed with cooking spray and set over medium-high heat, cook onions for 10 minutes or until they begin to brown and soften, stirring occasionally. Reduce heat to low; add remaining ingredients, except parsley. Cook for 15 to 20 minutes, stirring occasionally, until onions turn brown.

3. Stir half of the onion mixture into the potatoes; place in a serving dish. Scatter remaining onion mixture over top. Serve sprinkled with parsley.

PREP: About 10 mins.
COOK: About 35 mins.

MAKES 6 SERVINGS

MAKE AHEAD
Prepare mashed potatoes and onions up to 1 day in advance. Can be frozen for up to 1 month.

NUTRITIONAL ANALYSIS
PER SERVING
142 calories
4.2 g protein
3.4 g fat, total
1 g fat, saturated
23.6 g carbohydrates
112 mg sodium
3 mg cholesterol
3.9 g fibre

TIPS
The trick to creamy mashed potatoes is to warm the boiled and drained potatoes on low heat for a couple of minutes. This evaporates any excess water and dries out the potatoes. The result is a creamier consistency.

PREP: About 10 mins.
COOK: About 15 mins.

MAKES 6 SERVINGS

MAKE AHEAD
Prepare mashed potatoes up
to 1 day in advance. Heat
gently to warm. Can be frozen
for up to 1 month.

NUTRITIONAL ANALYSIS
PER SERVING
211 calories
6.3 g protein
6.8 g fat, total
0.8 g fat, saturated
31.1 g carbohydrates
396 mg sodium
0.3 mg cholesterol
5.5 g fibre

TIPS
Tahini can be bought in the
specialty section of most
supermarkets or in any
Middle Eastern store. Use
tahini in moderation since it
has an intense flavor.

hummus mashed potatoes with coriander

Hummus, a Middle Eastern dish made of puréed chick-peas, tahini, and seasonings, is a delicacy usually served as an appetizer with crackers. Combining the hummus basics with mashed potatoes produces a sensational dish. I love it with fish or meat.

2 medium Yukon Gold potatoes (about 1 lb), peeled and cubed
1/2 cup chicken or vegetable stock
2 tbsp tahini (sesame seed paste)
1 tbsp fresh lemon juice
1 tsp minced garlic
1 tbsp olive oil
2 cups rinsed and drained canned chick-peas
1/2 tsp salt
1/4 tsp freshly ground black pepper
2 tbsp chopped fresh coriander

1. Place potatoes in a saucepan; add cold water to cover. Bring to a boil; cook for 15 to 20 minutes or until tender when pierced with the tip of a sharp knife.
2. Meanwhile, process remaining ingredients, except coriander, in a food processor until smooth. Drain potatoes; mash. Stir in chick-pea purée and coriander.

eggplant seafood rolls

quick

Unless cooked properly, eggplant can lack flavor and texture, which explains why it's so often deep-fried or cooked with loads of oil. Filling it, as I have in this recipe, with a creamy pesto crabmeat mixture makes it a meal in itself.

1 large eggplant, unpeeled, sliced lengthwise into 6 slices
2 tsp vegetable oil
1/3 cup smooth 5% ricotta cheese
2 tbsp Rose's Light Pesto (see page 184) or store-bought
1 oz light cream cheese, softened
4 oz crabmeat or surimi, finely chopped
3/4 cup tomato pasta sauce
1 tbsp grated Parmesan cheese

GARNISH
1/4 cup chopped fresh parsley

1. Preheat oven to 400°F.
2. Brush eggplant slices with oil. Either on a barbecue or in a nonstick grill pan sprayed with cooking spray, cook over medium-high heat for about 8 minutes until soft, turning halfway.
3. In a food processor, process ricotta, pesto, and cream cheese until smooth. Add crab; purée until smooth. Spread mixture over eggplant; roll up eggplant slices from the short end. Fasten with toothpick if desired.
4. Pour half of the tomato sauce over bottom of an 8-inch square glass baking dish. Place eggplant rolls in dish, seam side down. Pour remaining sauce over top; sprinkle with cheese. Bake for 5 to 8 minutes just until hot. Serve sprinkled with parsley.

PREP: About 10 mins.
COOK: About 15 mins.

MAKES 6 SERVINGS

MAKE AHEAD
Prepare dish up to 1 day in advance. Heat gently. Or freeze for up to 6 weeks.

NUTRITIONAL ANALYSIS PER SERVING
136 calories
7.2 g protein
6.8 g fat, total
2 g fat, saturated
11.5 g carbohydrates
385 mg sodium
12 mg cholesterol
3 g fibre

TIP
I find I am always using surimi (imitation crabmeat). It tastes great, is more economical than crabmeat, and is readily available. Fresh crabmeat is more difficult to find and canned crabmeat does not have the best flavor.

baked mediterranean stuffed eggplant

This filling is delicious and could also be used to stuff zucchini or tomatoes.

PREP: About 15 mins.
COOK: About 45 mins.

MAKES 6 SERVINGS

MAKE AHEAD
Prepare entire dish up to
1 day in advance and bake
before serving. Or bake and
then refrigerate for up to
2 days. Filling can be made,
cooked, and frozen for up to
3 months.

NUTRITIONAL ANALYSIS
PER SERVING
219 calories
16.2 g protein
8.8 g fat, total
3 g fat, saturated
18.7 g carbohydrates
342 mg sodium
23 mg cholesterol
5.5 g fibre

TIP
For a vegetarian version,
replace the ground chicken or
beef with ground soy.

1 large eggplant (about 1-1/4 lb) or 2 small eggplants
2 tsp vegetable oil
1 cup chopped onions
2 tsp minced garlic
12 oz lean ground chicken or beef
3 tbsp grated Parmesan cheese
2 cups chopped plum tomatoes
1/4 cup chopped black olives
1/4 cup seasoned bread crumbs
1/4 cup chopped fresh parsley
1 tsp dried basil
1/2 tsp dried oregano
1/8 tsp each salt and freshly ground black pepper

GARNISH
1/4 cup chopped fresh parsley

1. Preheat oven to 375°F. Spray rimmed baking sheet with cooking spray.
2. Slice eggplant in half lengthwise. Place skin side up on prepared baking sheet. Bake larger eggplant for 20 minutes or just until soft, and smaller eggplants for 10 to 12 minutes. Scrape out pulp, leaving skin intact. Chop pulp; set aside.
3. Meanwhile, in a nonstick skillet sprayed with cooking spray, heat oil over medium-high heat; cook onions and garlic for 5 minutes or until onions begin to brown. Add reserved eggplant pulp and ground chicken; cook, stirring to break up chicken, for 5 minutes or until chicken is cooked through. Remove from heat. Add 2 tbsp of the Parmesan and all remaining ingredients, except the parsley; stir just until combined. Fill eggplant skins with chicken mixture; sprinkle with remaining Parmesan. Place filled eggplants on baking sheet; bake for 20 minutes or until hot. Serve sprinkled with parsley.

one-dish meals

creamy seafood and dill casserole over rice

PREP: About 15 mins.
COOK: About 12 mins.

MAKES 6 SERVINGS

MAKE AHEAD
The entire casserole can be made up to 1 day in advance, undercooking the seafood. After heating gently for 20 minutes in a 350°F oven, broil for 1 minute. You can also freeze this for up to 6 weeks.

NUTRITIONAL ANALYSIS PER SERVING
354 calories
26 g protein
4.8 g fat, total
1.2 g fat, saturated
50 g carbohydrates
400 mg sodium
95 mg cholesterol
2.6 g fibre

TIP
The key to the success of this recipe is to slightly undercook the seafood: overcooking makes seafood too tough.

My cooking school students rate this as my number one casserole. Usually, a seafood casserole is made with 35% whipping cream and butter. Neither is used here. Instead, it's the 2% evaporated milk combined with the cornstarch that makes a wonderful creamy sauce.

1-1/2 cups jasmine rice
  (cook rice while preparing rest of dish)
2-1/2 cups fish or chicken stock
1 cup 2% evaporated milk
1 tsp Dijon mustard
3 tbsp cornstarch
2 tsp vegetable oil
1 cup chopped onions

2 tsp minced garlic
1 cup chopped sweet red peppers
12 oz deveined peeled shrimp
12 oz scallops
1/3 cup chopped green onions
1/3 cup chopped fresh dill
2 tbsp grated Parmesan cheese
1/8 tsp each salt and pepper

TOPPING
3 tbsp dry seasoned bread crumbs
1 tbsp chopped fresh dill
2 tsp grated Parmesan cheese
1 tsp olive oil

1. Spray a 13- × 9-inch glass baking dish with cooking spray.
2. Bring rice and 1-1/2 cups stock to a boil. Simmer for 10 minutes, covered. Remove from heat; keep covered for 10 minutes. Fluff with a fork. Set aside.
3. In a bowl, mix together remaining stock, milk, mustard, and cornstarch until smooth. Set aside.
4. Preheat oven broiler. In a large nonstick skillet sprayed with cooking spray, heat oil over medium heat; cook onions and garlic for 3 minutes. Stir in peppers; cook for 2 minutes. Stir in seafood; cook over high heat until almost cooked through, about 3 minutes. Stir in milk mixture; cook until slightly thickened, about 3 minutes. Stir in green onions, dill, cheese, and salt and pepper. Pour casserole into prepared dish.
5. To make topping: Combine all topping ingredients. Sprinkle mixture over casserole. Broil for 1 minute or until golden. Serve alongside rice.

fresh salmon and hoisin burgers

For a change from regular meat burgers, these are a must. Fresh salmon burgers are amazing. The hoisin mayonnaise sauce is equally as good.

BURGERS

1 lb skinless boneless salmon fillet, cut into 1-inch pieces

1 egg

1/4 cup chopped fresh coriander or parsley

2 tbsp hoisin sauce

2 tbsp light mayonnaise

1/4 cup chopped green onions

1 tsp minced garlic

SAUCE

2 tbsp hoisin sauce

1 tbsp light mayonnaise

Boston lettuce leaves

1. To make burgers: In a food processor, process burger ingredients until coarsely ground by turning processor on and off. Do not purée. Form into 5 patties.
2. Either barbecue or, on a nonstick grill pan sprayed with cooking spray, grill burgers until medium done, about 3 minutes per side on medium heat.
3. To make sauce: In a small bowl, combine sauce ingredients.
4. Place lettuce leaves on a serving dish; top with burgers. Spread with sauce.

PREP: About 10 mins.
COOK: About 6 mins.

MAKES 5 SERVINGS

MAKE AHEAD

These burgers can be prepared 1 day in advance or frozen raw for 1 month. It's best to cook them just before serving.

NUTRITIONAL ANALYSIS
PER SERVING

186 calories

18 g protein

9 g fat, total

0.9 g fat, saturated

6 g carbohydrates

304 mg sodium

80 mg cholesterol

0.8 g fibre

TIPS

These burgers are best if not overcooked (it's safe to eat salmon undercooked, and that's the preferred and most delicious way to eat this fish). Wet your hands to make forming the burgers easier.

sushi burgers

PREP: About 15 mins.
COOK: About 25 mins.

MAKES 6 SERVINGS

MAKE AHEAD
These can be prepared early
in the day and sautéed just
before serving.

NUTRITIONAL ANALYSIS
PER SERVING
132 calories
8 g protein
3.7 g fat, total
0.7 g fat, saturated
21 g carbohydrates
186 mg sodium
49 mg cholesterol
1.2 g fibre

TIP
Surimi, or imitation crabmeat,
contains no shellfish
products, is kosher, and is
much less expensive than
crabmeat.

I love anything to do with sushi. I've created recipes such as sushi salad and smoked salmon and sushi pizza, so why not a burger? It's outstanding, delicious, and unique.

BURGERS
1 cup sushi rice
1 cup water
2 tbsp rice wine vinegar
6 oz crabmeat or surimi, chopped
2 tbsp light mayonnaise
2 tbsp soy sauce
1/2 cup dry unseasoned bread crumbs
1/3 cup chopped green onions
1/2 tsp wasabi (Japanese mustard)
1 egg
1 egg white
1 tsp sesame seeds
1 tsp vegetable oil

SAUCE
2 tbsp light sour cream
1 tbsp light mayonnaise
1/2 tsp wasabi (Japanese mustard)

GARNISH
Sliced cucumber and avocado

1. To make burgers: In a large pot on high heat, bring rice and water to boil. Cover, and simmer on lowest heat for 10 minutes. Let rest for 10 more minutes, covered. Add rice wine vinegar; cool rice just till still slightly warm. Keep covered with a wet tea towel if you must leave it for some time (never leave longer than 3 hours before serving).
2. Add crabmeat, mayonnaise, soy sauce, bread crumbs, green onions, wasabi, egg, and egg white; mix well. Using 1/3 cup for each, make 6 patties and sprinkle sesame seeds over top.
3. In a nonstick skillet sprayed with cooking spray, heat oil; sauté burgers for 3 minutes per side.
4. To make sauce: Mix ingredients together. Serve sauce and garnishes with burgers.

chicken paella with sausage, shrimp, and mussels

This is my version of paella, a rice, sausage, and seafood dish originating in Spain. Using skinless chicken breasts and draining the sausage after it's been cooked keeps the calories and fat to a minimum. The key to this dish is the Arborio rice, which gives it a wonderful, creamy texture.

12 oz boneless skinless chicken breast (about 3 breasts), cubed	1 cup short-grain Arborio rice
3 tbsp all-purpose flour	2-1/2 cups chicken stock
2 tsp vegetable oil	2 cups chopped plum tomatoes
6 oz mild Italian sausage, cut into 1/2-inch pieces	2 tsp dried basil
	1 tsp dried oregano
1 cup chopped onions	1 bay leaf
2 tsp minced garlic	1/2 tsp crumbled saffron threads (optional)
1 cup chopped sweet red peppers	1/8 tsp each salt and pepper
1 cup chopped sweet green peppers	6 oz deveined peeled shrimp
	12 mussels, scrubbed and beards removed

GARNISH
1/4 cup chopped fresh parsley (optional)

1. Dust chicken with flour. In a large nonstick skillet sprayed with cooking spray, heat oil over medium-high heat; cook chicken for 3 minutes, turning until browned but not cooked through. Remove from pan; respray pan with cooking spray. Cook sausage over medium-high heat for 5 minutes or until cooked through; remove from pan with a slotted spoon, leaving behind as much fat as possible. Set chicken and sausage aside. Wipe out pan and respray.

2. Cook onions and garlic over medium-high heat for 4 minutes or until softened. Stir in peppers; cook for 3 minutes. Stir in rice; cook for 1 minute. Add sausage, chicken stock, tomatoes, basil, oregano, bay leaf, saffron (if using), and salt and pepper. Bring to a boil. Cover, and simmer on low heat for 25 minutes, stirring occasionally.

3. Meanwhile, if using large or jumbo shrimp, cut in half. Add shrimp, mussels, and reserved chicken to sausage mixture; cook on a medium high heat for 5 minutes just until rice is soft and mussels have opened. (If rice begins to stick, add another 1/2 cup stock.) Discard bay leaf and any mussels that do not open. Garnish with parsley (if using).

PREP: About 20 mins.
COOK: About 45 mins.

MAKES 6 SERVINGS

MAKE AHEAD
Prepare early in the day up to the point before the seafood is added. Just before serving, add seafood and cook. Can be frozen without mussels for up to 6 weeks.

NUTRITIONAL ANALYSIS PER SERVING
407 calories
49 g protein
7.3 g fat, total
2.2 g fat, saturated
36 g carbohydrates
624 mg sodium
139 mg cholesterol
3 g fibre

TIP
This dish is also delicious with boneless chicken thighs.

chicken and bean mediterranean chili

PREP: About 10 mins.
COOK: About 40 mins.

MAKES 6 SERVINGS

MAKE AHEAD
Make up to 3 days ahead or
freeze for up to 2 months. If
frozen, defrost and reheat
gently until warm, about
10 minutes.

NUTRITIONAL ANALYSIS
PER SERVING
200 calories
15 g protein
4 g fat, total
1.4 g fat, saturated
42 g carbohydrates
530 mg sodium
25 mg cholesterol
10 g fibre

Chili is usually made with fatty ground beef. This version uses boneless chicken breast dusted with cornstarch, which keeps the chicken moist. The chick-peas are a nice variation on that chili standard, red kidney beans.

2 tsp vegetable oil

1-1/2 cups diced onions

2 cups sliced mushrooms

1 cup diced sweet green peppers

1 cup diced carrots

2 tsp minced garlic

12 oz boneless skinless chicken breast (about 3 breasts), diced

1/4 cup cornstarch

2 cups tomato pasta sauce

1 cup drained and rinsed canned chick-peas

1 cup chicken stock

2 tsp dried basil

2 tsp chili powder

1 tsp dried oregano

GARNISH
1/3 cup chopped fresh parsley (optional)

1. In a nonstick skillet, heat oil over medium heat; cook onions for 5 minutes or until lightly browned. Stir in mushrooms, green peppers, carrots, and garlic; cook for 10 minutes or just until vegetables are softened and mushrooms begin to brown.

2. Dust chicken with cornstarch and add to vegetable mixture. Cook for 5 minutes or just until chicken browns, stirring constantly.

3. Stir in remaining ingredients. Bring to boil, cover, and simmer for 20 minutes. Serve sprinkled with parsley (if using).

boneless chicken thigh cacciatore

One of my favorite cuts of chicken is boneless skinless chicken thigh. When dusted with flour and sautéed, it's so moist and delicious it tastes like beef tenderloin. You can now find this cut in supermarkets.

1 lb boneless skinless chicken thighs, cut into 1-inch cubes
1/4 cup all-purpose flour
2 tsp vegetable oil
1-1/2 cups diced onions
1 cup diced sweet green peppers
1 cup diced mushrooms
2 tsp minced garlic
1-1/2 tsp dried basil
1 tsp dried oregano
2 cups tomato pasta sauce
1/2 cup chicken stock
1/4 cup diced rehydrated sun-dried tomatoes
1 tbsp brown sugar

GARNISH
1/4 cup chopped fresh basil (optional)

1. Dust chicken with flour. In a nonstick skillet sprayed with cooking spray, heat oil over medium heat; cook chicken until seared and browned on all sides but not cooked all the way through, about 5 minutes. Remove from pan and set aside.

2. Respray skillet; cook onions for 5 minutes or until softened and browned. Stir in green peppers, mushrooms, and garlic; cook for 5 minutes or until vegetables are soft.

3. Stir in remaining ingredients and chicken. Bring to a boil, cover, and simmer on low heat for 15 minutes. Garnish with basil (if using) before serving.

PREP: About 10 mins.
COOK: About 30 mins.

MAKES 4 SERVINGS

MAKE AHEAD
Cook this dish up to 1 day in advance or freeze for up to 2 months. Defrost if frozen, then reheat gently for 10 minutes or until warm.

NUTRITIONAL ANALYSIS
PER SERVING
260 calories
28 g protein
8 g fat, total
4 g fat, saturated
27 g carbohydrates
424 mg sodium
110 mg cholesterol
5.4 g fibre

TIPS
Always buy dried sun-dried tomatoes, rather than those packed in oil, and rehydrate them by covering in water and microwaving for 1 minute on High, or by leaving them to soak in hot water for 15 minutes.

ratatouille meatloaf casserole with goat cheese topping

PREP: About 15 mins.
COOK: About 40 mins.

MAKES 6 SERVINGS

MAKE AHEAD
Prepare this meatloaf up to
1 day in advance. Bake just
before serving. Alternatively,
bake and freeze for up to
2 months. Defrost, and reheat
gently in a 300°F oven for
15 minutes.

NUTRITIONAL ANALYSIS
PER SERVING
227 calories
17 g protein
11 g fat, total
3.9 g fat, saturated
15 g carbohydrates
525 mg sodium
60 mg cholesterol
3.2 g fibre

TIP
When a dish is as flavorful
as this one, I tend to use a
plainer flavored tomato pasta
sauce.

I've never tasted a more delicious meatloaf. Forget the traditional Sunday classic—this one should replace it. Adding sautéed vegetables over the top keeps the meatloaf very moist. The goat cheese can be replaced by a cheese of your choice or by a soy cheese if you're lactose intolerant or keep kosher.

MEAT MIXTURE
12 oz lean ground beef
1/4 cup dry seasoned bread crumbs
3 tbsp barbecue sauce
1-1/2 tsp minced garlic
1 egg

VEGETABLE MIXTURE
2 tsp vegetable oil
1-1/2 cups chopped eggplant, unpeeled
1 cup chopped zucchini
1/2 cup chopped onions
1-1/2 tsp minced garlic
1 cup sliced mushrooms
1-1/2 cups tomato pasta sauce
1/4 cup sliced black olives
1-1/2 tsp dried basil
1 tsp dried oregano

2 oz goat cheese

1. Preheat oven to 350°F. Spray an 8-inch square baking dish with cooking spray.
2. To make meat mixture: In a large bowl, combine all ingredients. Press into prepared dish.
3. To make vegetable mixture: In a large nonstick skillet sprayed with cooking spray, heat oil over medium heat; cook eggplant, zucchini, onions, and garlic for 8 minutes, stirring often, or until softened. Stir in mushrooms; cook for 2 minutes. Stir in tomato sauce, olives, basil, and oregano; simmer for 2 minutes. Pour mixture over meat.
4. Bake, uncovered, in centre of oven for 25 minutes or until beef is cooked through. Dot with goat cheese. Bake another 5 minutes.

greek chili with black olives and feta cheese

Chili is the perfect comfort food. In this recipe, I use lean beef or lamb instead of regular ground beef, and only 1 teaspoon of oil. If you want to make the dish vegetarian, try using ground soy, found in the produce section of your supermarket. The beans add fibre and plant protein. This chili is delicious on its own or can be served over rice, couscous, or polenta.

1 tsp vegetable oil
1 cup chopped onions
1-1/2 cups chopped eggplant, unpeeled
1 cup chopped zucchini
1 cup sliced mushrooms
1 cup chopped sweet green peppers
2 tsp minced garlic
8 oz lean ground beef or lamb
1 cup rinsed and drained canned red kidney beans
1 cup rinsed and drained canned white kidney beans
1 can (19 oz) tomatoes, puréed
1-1/2 cups beef or chicken stock
1/3 cup sliced black olives
1 tbsp chili powder
1-1/2 tsp each dried basil and oregano

GARNISH
2 oz light feta cheese, crumbled
1/4 cup chopped fresh parsley

1. In a large nonstick saucepan sprayed with cooking spray, heat oil over medium heat; cook onions for 5 minutes or until lightly browned. Add eggplant, zucchini, mushrooms, green peppers, and garlic; sauté for 8 minutes, or until vegetables are softened, stirring occasionally. Stir in beef; cook for 2 minutes, stirring to break it up, or until no longer pink. Drain excess fat.

2. In a large bowl, mash 1/2 cup red kidney beans with 1/2 cup white kidney beans. Stir mashed and whole beans, tomatoes, stock, olives, chili powder, basil, and oregano into beef mixture. Bring to a boil. Reduce heat to low, cover, and simmer for 30 minutes. Serve sprinkled with feta and parsley.

PREP: About 10 mins.
COOK: About 45 mins.

MAKES 6 SERVINGS

MAKE AHEAD
Prepare up to 1 day in advance or freeze for up to 2 months. If frozen, defrost then reheat gently until warm.

NUTRITIONAL ANALYSIS PER SERVING
245 calories
16 g protein
8 g fat, total
2.4 g fat, saturated
26 g carbohydrates
650 mg sodium
17 mg cholesterol
6.1 g fibre

TIP
If using canned whole tomatoes, place contents in food processor or blender to "crush."

beef and sautéed corn chili

Sautéing the corn until it is brown makes this chili so distinctive in taste. Feel free to make it vegetarian by substituting ground soy, found in the produce section of your supermarket.

PREP: About 10 mins.
COOK: About 40 mins.

MAKES 6 SERVINGS

MAKE AHEAD
This chili can be prepared up to 1 day in advance or frozen for up to 2 months. Defrost and reheat gently.

NUTRITIONAL ANALYSIS
PER SERVING
320 calories
18 g protein
7 g fat, total
2 g fat, saturated
40 g carbohydrates
300 mg sodium
16 mg cholesterol
7 g fibre

TIPS
For a beautiful presentation, serve the chili in kaiser or other bread rolls. Cut the top off the roll and remove the soft bread, leaving the outer crust intact. Fill with chili.

2 tsp vegetable oil

1-1/2 cups chopped onions

1 cup drained canned corn

2 tsp minced garlic

8 oz extra lean ground beef

1 can (19 oz) red kidney beans, rinsed and drained

2-1/2 cups tomato pasta sauce

1 cup diced potato

1/2 cup chicken or beef stock

2 tsp chili powder

1-1/2 tsp dried basil

1 tsp brown sugar

1/2 tsp cumin

GARNISH
1/4 cup chopped fresh parsley (optional)

1. In a nonstick skillet sprayed with cooking spray, heat oil over medium heat; cook onions for 5 minutes or until soft. Stir in corn and garlic; cook for 8 minutes or until corn is browned. Stir in beef; cook for 5 minutes or just until beef is cooked.

2. Stir in remaining ingredients. Bring to a boil, reduce heat, and simmer, covered, for 25 to 30 minutes or just until potatoes are soft. Serve sprinkled with parsley (if using).

basil meatloaf with yukon gold potato topping

Liven up your dinner with this delicious meatloaf. The Yukon Gold potatoes make it so creamy you'd think it contained butter. Serve it right out of the pan.

MASHED POTATOES

1-1/2 medium Yukon Gold potatoes,
   peeled and cubed (about 2 cups)
   (boil potatoes while meat is baking)

2 tsp vegetable oil

1 cup diced onions

1/4 cup light sour cream

2 tsp olive oil

1 tsp crushed garlic

1/2 tsp dried basil leaves

1/4 tsp salt

TOPPING

1 tbsp grated Parmesan cheese

1 tbsp barbecue sauce

MEATLOAF

12 oz extra lean ground beef

1 egg

1/3 cup barbecue sauce

1/4 cup dry seasoned bread crumbs

1/4 cup finely diced green onions

1-1/2 tsp crushed garlic

1 tsp dried basil leaves

1/8 tsp each salt and pepper

1. Preheat oven to 375°F. Spray an 8- × 4-inch loaf pan with cooking spray.
2. To make mashed potatoes: Cover potatoes with water in a saucepan; boil for 15 minutes or just until tender. Drain and mash well. In a nonstick skillet sprayed with cooking spray, heat oil over medium heat; cook onions for 8 minutes or until browned. Stir into potatoes along with remaining ingredients, mixing just until combined.
3. To make meatloaf: In a bowl, combine meatloaf ingredients. Pat into loaf pan. Bake for 30 minutes. Remove from oven; spread mashed potatoes over top. Sprinkle with Parmesan cheese and drizzle with barbecue sauce. Bake another 15 minutes. Let rest 10 minutes before slicing.

PREP: About 15 mins.
COOK: About 1 h.

MAKES 6 SERVINGS

MAKE AHEAD
This dish can be baked up to 1 day in advance. Gently reheat in a 300°F oven for 15 minutes. Alternatively, freeze meatloaf for up to 1 month. Defrost, then reheat gently until warm.

NUTRITIONAL ANALYSIS PER SERVING
222 calories
14 g protein
9 g fat, total
3 g fat, saturated
19 g carbohydrates
200 mg sodium
50 mg cholesterol
2.3 g fibre

TIP
Always store potatoes in a cool dark drawer, never in the refrigerator.

tex mex meatloaf rolled with corn, onion, and cheese

This Southwestern-inspired meatloaf is delicious and unique. The salsa, along with sautéed corn and cheese, adds a whole new twist to the standard meatloaf. Use hot salsa if you like some spice in your life.

MEATLOAF
1 lb extra lean ground beef
1 egg
1/3 cup medium salsa
1/4 cup dry seasoned bread crumbs
1/4 cup chopped fresh coriander
1-1/2 tsp minced garlic
1/2 tsp cumin

FILLING
3/4 cup diced onions
1/2 cup drained canned corn
1/2 cup diced sweet red peppers
1/4 cup shredded light mozzarella cheese

TOPPING
1/4 cup medium salsa

1. Preheat oven to 375°F. Spray an 8- × 4-inch loaf pan with cooking spray.
2. To make meatloaf: In a bowl, combine ingredients. On a 12-inch square piece of waxed paper, pat out mixture into an 8-inch square.
3. To make filling: In a nonstick skillet sprayed with cooking spray, cook onions over medium heat for 5 minutes or until softened. Stir in corn; cook 5 to 8 minutes or until corn begins to brown. Stir in red peppers; cook for 3 minutes or until softened. Spread over meatloaf and sprinkle with cheese. Using the waxed paper as a guide, roll up the meatloaf; carefully place in loaf pan seam side down. Spoon salsa over top.
4. Bake for 40 to 45 minutes or until meat is well cooked. Let rest 10 minutes before carefully inverting onto a serving platter. Slice.

PREP: About 15 mins.
COOK: About 55 mins.

MAKES 6 SERVINGS

MAKE AHEAD
Bake meatloaf up to 1 day in advance or freeze for up to 2 months. If frozen, defrost before reheating gently in a 300°F oven for 10 minutes or until warm.

NUTRITIONAL ANALYSIS
PER SERVING
200 calories
18 g protein
7 g fat, total
3 g fat, saturated
10 g carbohydrates
320 mg sodium
55 mg cholesterol
2.2 g fibre

spinach and ricotta cheese rolled meatloaf

Here's a great way to get vegetables into your meal. The spinach and ricotta make an outstanding filling and look beautiful.

MEATLOAF

1 lb extra lean ground beef

1/4 cup dry seasoned bread crumbs

1/4 cup barbecue sauce

1/4 cup finely diced green onions

3 tbsp chopped fresh parsley

1 egg

2 tsp minced garlic

1/2 tsp dried oregano

1/8 tsp each salt and pepper

TOPPING

2 tbsp barbecue sauce

2 tsp grated Parmesan cheese

FILLING

1 cup diced onions

1/3 cup thawed and drained frozen chopped spinach

1-1/2 tsp crushed garlic

2/3 cup 5% smooth ricotta cheese

1 oz light cream cheese

1 tbsp grated Parmesan cheese

1. Preheat oven to 375°F. Spray an 8- × 4-inch loaf pan with cooking spray.
2. To make meatloaf: In a bowl, mix all meatloaf ingredients. On a 12-inch square piece of waxed paper, pat out mixture into an 8-inch square.
3. To make filling: In a nonstick skillet sprayed with cooking spray, cook onions over medium heat for 5 minutes until lightly browned. Stir in spinach and garlic; cook for 2 minutes. Turn off heat; add cheeses, stirring until combined. Spread over meatloaf. Using the waxed paper as a guide, roll up the meatloaf; carefully place in loaf pan seam side down. Spread barbecue sauce over top; sprinkle with cheese.
4. Bake 40 to 45 minutes. Let rest for 10 minutes before carefully inverting onto a serving platter. Slice.

PREP: About 15 mins.
COOK: About 45 mins.

MAKES 6 SERVINGS

MAKE AHEAD
This meatloaf can be baked up to 1 day in advance or frozen for up to 1 month. If frozen, defrost, then gently reheat in a 300°F oven for 10 minutes or until warm.

NUTRITIONAL ANALYSIS PER SERVING
198 calories
16 g protein
7 g fat, total
3 g fat, saturated
9 g carbohydrates
400 mg sodium
61 mg cholesterol
1.3 g fibre

TIPS
Always buy an extra-smooth ricotta cheese, which is easier to mix. A 5% milk fat version is now available.

super quick

PREP: About 10 mins.
COOK: About 10 mins.

MAKES 5 SERVINGS

MAKE AHEAD
Prepare burgers up to 1 day in advance or freeze, separately wrapped, for up to 2 months. Grill, without defrosting, just before serving.

NUTRITIONAL ANALYSIS PER SERVING
192 calories
19 g protein
9 g fat, total
2.9 g fat, saturated
8 g carbohydrates
398 mg sodium
68 mg cholesterol
1.3 g fibre

TIPS
Never buy sun-dried tomatoes packed in oil: they are loaded with calories and fat. It's always best to buy the dried kind that comes in bags.

sun-dried tomato burgers

The sun-dried tomatoes give this burger the best flavor. I like to buy sun-dried tomatoes in bulk and keep them in the freezer. To rehydrate them, I either soak them in hot water for 15 minutes or cover them with water and microwave on High for 1 minute. The sauce is outstanding as well.

BURGERS
1 lb extra lean ground beef
1/4 cup dry seasoned bread crumbs
1/4 cup chopped rehydrated sun-dried tomatoes
3 tbsp barbecue sauce or ketchup
1 egg
2 tsp minced garlic
1 tsp dried basil
1/2 tsp dried oregano

SAUCE
3 tbsp barbecue sauce
2 tsp light mayonnaise

GARNISH
Sliced onions, pickles, tomatoes, and lettuce

1. To make burgers: In a large bowl, combine all burger ingredients. Form into 5 patties. On a grill sprayed with cooking spray, cook patties on one side over medium heat for 7 minutes. Turn and cook 3 to 8 minutes longer or until cooked through. (Alternatively, bake in preheated 450°F oven for 10 to 15 minutes or until cooked through, turning once.)
2. To make sauce: In a small bowl, mix sauce ingredients. Serve over top of burgers with garnishes.

hoisin garlic burgers

This is another great burger that tastes of Asia. Hoisin sauce is delicious over the beef. Be certain to use lean ground beef, which has only 10 percent fat; regular ground beef can have more than 35 percent fat.

BURGERS

1 lb lean ground beef

1/4 cup dry seasoned bread crumbs

1/4 cup chopped green onions

3 tbsp chopped fresh coriander or parsley

2 tbsp hoisin sauce

1 tsp minced gingerroot

1 tsp minced garlic

1 egg

GLAZE

2 tbsp water

2 tbsp hoisin sauce

1 tsp sesame oil

1. To make burgers: In a bowl, stir together all burger ingredients. Form into 5 patties.
2. To make glaze: In a small bowl, whisk together glaze ingredients. Brush half over tops of patties. Preheat barbecue. On grill sprayed with cooking spray, cook patties brushed side down over medium heat for 7 minutes. Brush with remaining sauce; turn and cook 3 to 8 minutes longer or until cooked through. (Alternatively, bake in preheated 450°F oven for 10 to 15 minutes or until cooked through, turning once.)

PREP: About 5 mins.

COOK: About 10 mins.

MAKES 5 SERVINGS

MAKE AHEAD

Prepare burgers up to 1 day in advance or freeze, separately wrapped, for up to 6 months. Grill, without defrosting, just before serving.

NUTRITIONAL ANALYSIS PER SERVING

217 calories

21 g protein

11 g fat, total

3.8 g fat, saturated

8.6 g carbohydrates

376 mg sodium

76 mg cholesterol

0.6 g fibre

TIP

For a lower-fat version, try ground chicken, turkey, or veal.

stir-fries

PREP: About 15 mins.
COOK: About 15 mins.

MAKE 4 SERVINGS

MAKE AHEAD
Prepare sauce up to 3 days
in advance. Freeze for up to
2 months. The stir-fry can be
frozen for up to 1 month.

NUTRITIONAL ANALYSIS
PER SERVING
130 calories
7.6 g protein
2 g fat, total
0.3 g fat, saturated
20 g carbohydrates
200 mg sodium
43 mg cholesterol
1.5 g fibre

TIP
If you don't have plum sauce,
substitute hoisin sauce.

seafood stir-fry with plum and sweet chili sauce

The texture of the asparagus, baby corn, and water chestnuts makes this a wonderful stir-fry. The sweet-sour sauce over the seafood blends beautifully with its flavor. Serve over rice or noodles.

SAUCE
1/3 cup corn syrup
1/3 cup plum sauce
3 tbsp rice wine vinegar
2 tbsp sweet chili sauce or ketchup
2 tbsp soy sauce
1-1/2 tsp minced garlic
1 tsp minced gingerroot
1 tsp cornstarch

STIR-FRY
12 oz deveined peeled shrimp, scallops, or other firm fish, cut into small bite-sized pieces
2 tsp vegetable oil
1 cup chopped onions
2 cups chopped asparagus
1 cup chopped drained canned baby corn
1/2 cup sliced water chestnuts

GARNISH
1/4 cup chopped fresh coriander or parsley
1 tbsp chopped toasted cashews

1. To make sauce: In a bowl, mix sauce ingredients together until cornstarch is dissolved. Set aside.
2. To make stir-fry: In a nonstick wok sprayed with cooking spray, cook shrimp on high heat for 2 minutes. Do not cook through. Set aside.
3. Respray wok. Add oil and onions; stir-fry for 5 minutes. Add asparagus, corn, and water chestnuts; stir-fry for 2 minutes or until asparagus begins to turn bright green. Add sauce and shrimp; stir-fry just until sauce begins to thicken, about 3 minutes. Transfer to a serving platter and sprinkle with garnishes.

tuna stir-fry with coconut thai sauce

There's nothing like the texture and taste of fresh grilled or seared tuna. The key is not to over-cook it. In fact, serving it slightly rare is the only way to go! Combining light coconut milk and hoisin makes for a creamy Asian sauce.

SAUCE

3/4 cup light coconut milk

1/4 cup hoisin sauce

1-1/2 tbsp honey

1-1/2 tsp sesame oil

1-1/2 tbsp soy sauce

2 tsp rice wine vinegar

1-1/2 tsp minced garlic

1 tsp minced gingerroot

STIR-FRY

12 oz fresh tuna steak

1-1/2 cups sliced sweet red peppers

1-1/2 cups sugar snap peas or snow peas

GARNISH

1/3 cup chopped green onions

1/4 cup chopped fresh coriander

2 tsp toasted sesame seeds

1. To make sauce: In a bowl, mix sauce ingredients together until smooth. Set aside.
2. To make stir-fry: In a nonstick skillet or grill pan sprayed with cooking spray, cook tuna on high heat just until seared on both sides but still rare on the inside, about 3 minutes. Immediately remove from skillet; set aside. Cut into 1-inch cubes.
3. In a nonstick skillet or wok sprayed with cooking spray, stir-fry peppers and peas on high heat for 3 minutes. Add sauce and tuna; stir-fry for 2 minutes. Do not overcook tuna. Transfer to a serving platter and sprinkle with garnishes.

PREP: About 10 mins.
COOK: About 10 mins.

MAKES 4 SERVINGS

MAKE AHEAD
Prepare sauce up to 3 days in advance. Freeze for up to 2 months. Stir-fry just before serving. Stir-fry can be frozen for up to 1 month.

NUTRITIONAL ANALYSIS
PER SERVING
250 calories
22 g protein
3 g fat, total
0.6 g fat, saturated
34 g carbohydrates
360 mg sodium
35 mg cholesterol
2 g fibre

TIP
Always use light coconut milk, which has 75 percent less fat than regular canned coconut milk.

scallop and pineapple sesame stir-fry

PREP: About 12 mins.
COOK: About 10 mins.

MAKES 4 SERVINGS

MAKE AHEAD
Prepare sauce up to 3 days
in advance. Freeze for up to
2 months. Stir-fry just before
serving. Freeze leftovers for
up to 1 month.

NUTRITIONAL ANALYSIS
PER SERVING
285 calories
15 g protein
5 g fat, total
0.6 g fat, saturated
40 g carbohydrates
450 mg sodium
24 mg cholesterol
2 g fibre

TIPS
Always keep frozen pineapple
or orange juice concentrate
on hand so that you can make
juice when you need some.
You can refreeze these concentrates and use just the
amount you need.

I always use large sea scallops, which are more tender and sweeter than bay scallops. If the scallops you have are large, slice them in half. Feel free to substitute large shrimp. If fresh pineapple isn't available, use either canned chunks packed in their own juice or another fresh fruit such as mango or pear.

SAUCE
1/2 cup pineapple or orange juice
1/3 cup honey
3 tbsp soy sauce
2 tbsp rice wine vinegar
1 tbsp cornstarch
2 tsp sesame oil
1 tsp minced garlic
1/2 tsp hot sauce

STIR-FRY
12 oz sea scallops
1/4 cup cornstarch
2 tsp vegetable oil
1-1/2 cups sliced sweet red peppers
1-1/2 cups sliced sweet yellow, orange, or green peppers
1-1/2 cups sliced snow peas

GARNISH
1/2 cup diced fresh pineapple
1/4 cup chopped fresh coriander or parsley
1-1/2 tsp sesame seeds

1. To make sauce: In a bowl, mix sauce ingredients together until smooth. Set aside.
2. To make stir-fry: Dust scallops with cornstarch. In a nonstick wok or skillet sprayed with cooking spray, heat oil on high; stir-fry scallops for 3 minutes or until browned on all sides. Do not cook through. Remove and set aside.
3. Respray wok. Add peppers and snow peas; stir-fry for 3 minutes. Add sauce and scallops; stir-fry for 3 minutes or until sauce thickens. Transfer to a serving platter and sprinkle with garnishes.

chicken stir-fry with hoisin plum sauce

I found that the perfect way to maintain the tenderness of chicken in a stir-fry, without using lots of oil or butter, is to coat it in cornstarch or flour. You'll be amazed at how tender the chicken morsels are.

SAUCE
1/2 cup plum sauce
1/4 cup hoisin sauce
2 tbsp soy sauce
3 tbsp water
1 tbsp brown sugar
1-1/2 tsp minced garlic
1 tsp chopped gingerroot

STIR-FRY
12 oz boneless skinless chicken breast (about 3 breasts), cubed
3 tbsp cornstarch
2 tsp vegetable oil
2 cups sliced sweet red peppers
1-1/2 cups sliced sweet green peppers
1 cup sliced water chestnuts

GARNISH
1/4 cup chopped fresh coriander or basil
2 tbsp toasted chopped cashews or peanuts

1. To make sauce: In a bowl, mix sauce ingredients together until smooth. Set aside.
2. To make stir-fry: Dust chicken with cornstarch. In a nonstick skillet sprayed with cooking spray, heat oil; sear chicken just until browned on all sides, about 5 minutes. Remove and set aside.
3. Respray pan. Add peppers; stir-fry for 5 minutes, just until softened. Add water chestnuts, sauce, and chicken; cook on medium heat for 3 minutes just until chicken is cooked and sauce coats mixture. Transfer to a serving platter and sprinkle with garnishes.

PREP: About 15 mins.
COOK: About 15 mins.

MAKES 4 SERVINGS

MAKE AHEAD
Prepare sauce up to 4 days in advance. Freeze for up to 3 months. Freeze stir-fry for up to 1 month.

NUTRITIONAL ANALYSIS PER SERVING
290 calories
20 g protein
6 g fat, total
1 g fat, saturated
35 g carbohydrates
450 mg sodium
45 mg cholesterol
3 g fibre

TIPS
To easily toast nuts, heat in a small skillet on high heat for 2 minutes or just until lightly browned. I often toast a large amount of nuts and freeze them so that they are always available.

PREP: About 10 mins.
COOK: About 15 mins.

MAKES 4 SERVINGS

MAKE AHEAD
Prepare sauce up to 4 days
in advance. Freeze for up to
2 months. Stir-fry can be
frozen for up to 1 month.

NUTRITIONAL ANALYSIS
PER SERVING
370 calories
22 g protein
8 g fat, total
3 g fat, saturated
40 g carbohydrates
510 mg sodium
46 mg cholesterol
2 g fibre

TIP
You can replace the chicken
with pork.

coconut chicken over rice

This dish, with the flavors of coconut milk, fish sauce, coriander, and ginger, reminds me of a Thai stir-fry. The coconut milk and oyster sauce penetrate the chicken and make it incredibly moist. The key is coating the chicken with flour. Be sure not to overcook the peppers.

1 cup basmati rice (cook rice while preparing stir-fry)   1 cup chicken or vegetable stock

STIR-FRY
4 tsp vegetable oil
1 cup chopped onions
1-1/2 tsp minced garlic
1 tsp minced gingerroot
1 cup thinly sliced sweet red peppers
3/4 cup thinly sliced sweet green peppers
12 oz boneless skinless chicken breast (about 3 breasts), cut into 1-inch cubes
2 tbsp all-purpose flour

SAUCE   GARNISH
1 cup light coconut milk   1/3 cup chopped fresh coriander
2 tbsp fish sauce or oyster sauce
1 tsp cornstarch
1/4 to 1/2 tsp hot Asian chili sauce

1. In a medium saucepan, combine rice and stock. Bring to a boil. Reduce heat to medium-low; cover, and cook for 10 minutes. Remove from heat. Let stand covered for 10 minutes. Fluff with a fork.

2. To make stir-fry: In a large nonstick skillet, heat 2 tsp of the oil over medium-high heat; cook onions, garlic, and gingerroot for 5 minutes, or until onions are browned. Add peppers; cook for 5 minutes or until peppers are softened. Transfer mixture to a bowl.

3. Dust chicken with flour. Spray the skillet with cooking spray. Heat remaining oil over medium-high heat; cook chicken for 3 minutes or until browned on all sides.

4. To make sauce: In a small bowl, mix sauce ingredients until smooth. Add to skillet along with chicken and bring to a boil. Reduce heat, cover, and simmer for 2 minutes or until chicken is cooked through and mixture thickens. Stir in onion mixture. Serve chicken alongside rice, garnished with coriander.

mango beef stir-fry

The aroma of fish sauce is much stronger than its flavor once it's cooked. If you can't find fish sauce, use either soy sauce or oyster sauce. The steaks I like to use are sirloin, rib-eye, filet, or New York strip. The most delicious mangoes are from Indonesia. They're sweet and tender.

SAUCE

1/2 cup light coconut milk

1/4 cup hoisin sauce

3 tbsp brown sugar

2 tbsp fish sauce or soy sauce

1 tbsp natural peanut butter

1 tbsp water

2 tsp cornstarch

1-1/2 tsp minced garlic

1 tsp minced gingerroot

GARNISH

1/2 cup diced mangoes

1/4 cup chopped fresh coriander

3 tbsp chopped green onions

STIR-FRY

12 oz boneless grilling steak

2 tsp vegetable oil

1-1/2 cups sliced onions

2 cups sliced sweet red peppers

1. To make sauce: In a bowl, mix sauce ingredients together until smooth. Set aside.
2. To make stir-fry: On a barbecue or in a nonstick grill pan sprayed with cooking spray, grill beef on high heat until medium-rare, about 5 to 8 minutes. Slice steak thinly and keep covered.
3. In a nonstick skillet sprayed with cooking spray, heat oil over medium heat; stir-fry onions for 5 minutes or until softened. Add peppers; stir-fry for 3 minutes.
4. Add sauce and beef; stir-fry for 2 minutes or until sauce thickens, being careful not to overcook the beef. Transfer to a serving platter and sprinkle with garnishes.

PREP: About 10 mins.
COOK: About 18 mins.

MAKES 4 SERVINGS

MAKE AHEAD
Prepare sauce up to 3 days in advance. Freeze for up to 2 months. Stir-fry just before serving. Stir-fry can be frozen up to 1 month.

NUTRITIONAL ANALYSIS PER SERVING
290 calories
18 g protein
9 g fat, total
3 g fat, saturated
28 g carbohydrates
460 mg sodium
48 mg cholesterol
3 g fibre

TIPS
Fish sauce can be found in the Asian section of most supermarkets. Once opened, store the sauce in the refrigerator.

PREP: About 10 mins.
COOK: About 8 mins.

MAKES 4 SERVINGS

MAKE AHEAD
Prepare sauce up to 4 days in advance. Freeze for up to 3 months. Stir-fry just before serving. Stir-fry can be frozen for up to 1 month.

NUTRITIONAL ANALYSIS PER SERVING
161 calories
10 g protein
7.7 g fat, total
2.5 g fat, saturated
25 g carbohydrates
450 mg sodium
15 mg cholesterol
3 g fibre

TIPS
Be sure not to overcook the broccoli, snow peas, and red peppers. Try replacing the beef with chicken, pork, or firm tofu. The vegetables can also be of your choice.

chinese beef with crisp vegetables

This sauce, made from readily available ingredients, is so simple yet so delicious. Use the best quality steak, such as rib-eye, sirloin, filet, or New York. The colors and textures of this stir-fry give it not only a fabulous taste, but also great eye appeal. Serve this stir-fry over steamed rice, noodles, or couscous.

SAUCE
3/4 cup beef or chicken stock
1/4 cup packed brown sugar
2 tbsp low-sodium soy sauce
2 tbsp rice wine vinegar
2 tsp sesame oil
1 tbsp cornstarch
2 tsp minced garlic
1-1/2 tsp minced gingerroot

STIR-FRY
12 oz boneless grilling steak
2 tsp vegetable oil
1-1/2 cups chopped broccoli
1-1/2 cups thinly sliced sweet red peppers
1-1/2 cups snow peas

GARNISH
1/4 cup chopped fresh coriander or parsley
1/4 cup chopped green onions
2 tbsp chopped toasted cashews (optional)

1. To make sauce: In a bowl, mix sauce ingredients together until smooth. Set aside.
2. To make stir-fry: In a large nonstick skillet sprayed with cooking spray, cook beef on high heat for 3 minutes or until beef is browned but still rare. Let rest for 5 minutes; slice thinly.
3. Respray pan. Add oil, broccoli, peppers, and snow peas; cook for 2 minutes. Return beef to pan. After stirring sauce, add it to pan; cook for 2 minutes, stirring constantly, or until sauce is thickened and bubbly and beef is medium or to your liking, being careful not to overcook. Garnish with coriander, green onions, and toasted cashews (if using).

pasta and rice

PREP: 15 mins.
COOK: About 10 mins.

MAKES 4 SERVINGS

MAKE AHEAD
Mix all ingredients—except
pasta—early in the day.
When ready to serve, toss
with just-cooked or reheated
pasta to melt cheese.

NUTRITIONAL ANALYSIS
PER SERVING
381 calories
17.8 g protein
14 g fat, total
6 g fat, saturated
37.9 g carbohydrates
510 mg sodium
26.4 mg cholesterol
3.4 g fibre

TIPS
If you ever need to make your
pasta early in the day, rinse
with cold water and drain.
When ready to serve, run
cooked pasta under hot water
for 30 seconds, and then add
the rest of your ingredients.

linguine with tomatoes and three cheeses

Serving this pasta warm melts the cheese and just heats the tomatoes to a point where they're slightly softened. The variety of cheeses makes this an outstanding pasta dish.

8 oz linguine (cook pasta while preparing rest of dish)
2 cups diced plum tomatoes
2 oz goat cheese, crumbled
3/4 cup shredded low-fat mozzarella cheese
1/2 cup chopped green onions
1/2 cup chopped fresh basil (or 1-1/2 tsp dried basil)
1/4 cup grated Parmesan or Asiago cheese
2 tbsp olive oil
1 tsp minced garlic
Pinch each salt and pepper

In a large pot of boiling water, cook linguine for 8 to 10 minutes or until tender but firm. Drain and place in a serving bowl. Add remaining ingredients; toss.

pasta, tomatoes, and goat cheese

This is a simple pasta dish in which the goat cheese melts when added to the hot pasta just before serving. Plum tomatoes, instead of extra oil, give the dish the moisture it needs.

12 oz penne (cook pasta while preparing rest of dish)

3 oz goat cheese

2 tbsp olive oil

1 tbsp balsamic vinegar

1 tsp minced garlic

1/2 tsp hot pepper sauce

1/4 tsp each salt and freshly ground black pepper

3 cups diced plum tomatoes, seeded and diced (about 1-1/4 lb)

1/3 cup thinly sliced rehydrated sun-dried tomatoes

1/4 cup chopped green onions

1/4 cup chopped fresh basil (or 1 tsp dried basil)

1. In a large pot of boiling water, cook penne for 8 to 10 minutes or until tender but firm. Drain.
2. In a large bowl, mash together the goat cheese, olive oil, vinegar, garlic, hot pepper sauce, and salt and pepper. Stir in the tomatoes, green onions, and basil.
3. Add pasta to tomato mixture; toss to coat. Serve warm or at room temperature.

super quick

PREP: About 10 mins.
COOK: About 10 mins.

MAKES 6 SERVINGS

MAKE AHEAD
Prepare all ingredients, except pasta, early in the day. Cook pasta just before serving.

NUTRITIONAL ANALYSIS PER SERVING
320 calories
11 g protein
8.6 g fat, total
2.8 g fat, saturated
49 g carbohydrates
226 mg sodium
6.5 mg cholesterol
2.8 g fibre

TIPS
Instead of plum tomatoes, you can always use field tomatoes. Just be sure to seed them to get rid of excess moisture. To rehydrate sun-dried tomatoes, soak them in boiling water for 10 minutes, or cover them with water and microwave on High for 1 minute. Drain and then slice.

two-mushroom and feta cheese lasagna

PREP: About 15 mins.
COOK: About 45 mins.

MAKES 10 SERVINGS

MAKE AHEAD
Prepare lasagna, without baking, and freeze for up to 2 weeks. If lasagna ingredients have been frozen, thaw then bake. You can also prepare the cheese mixture and the sauce up to 2 days before preparing the lasagna.

NUTRITIONAL ANALYSIS
PER SERVING
296 calories
18 g protein
12 g fat, total
5.6 g fat, saturated
28 g carbohydrates
510 mg sodium
29 mg cholesterol
2.3 g fibre

TIPS
This white sauce doesn't call for the standard butter. Just be sure to mix well before heating to make sure the flour completely dissolves.

This is an outstanding vegetarian lasagna that can be served either as a main meal with a salad or as a side dish. I often serve it as part of a hot buffet. Using a combination of regular and oyster mushrooms gives the lasagna a wonderful taste and texture. Use whichever mushroom variety you prefer.

9 lasagna noodles (cook pasta while preparing rest of dish)

CHEESE MIXTURE
2 cups smooth light ricotta cheese
1 cup shredded low-fat mozzarella cheese
1/2 cup low-fat milk
3 tbsp grated Parmesan cheese
1/2 tsp freshly ground black pepper

SAUCE
2 tsp vegetable oil
1 cup chopped onions
2 tsp minced garlic
2 tsp dried oregano
4 cups sliced button mushrooms (about 12 oz)
4 cups sliced oyster mushrooms (about 12 oz)
1/2 cup sliced black olives
1/2 cup chopped rehydrated sun-dried tomatoes
4 oz light feta cheese, crumbled
1 cup cold vegetable stock
1 cup 2% evaporated milk
1/4 cup all-purpose flour
1-1/2 tsp Dijon mustard

TOPPING
2 tbsp grated Parmesan cheese

1. Preheat oven to 375°F. Spray a 13- × 9-inch baking dish with cooking spray.
2. In a large pot of boiling water, cook lasagna noodles for 12 to 14 minutes or until tender. Drain. Rinse under cold running water; drain and set aside.
3. To make cheese mixture: In a bowl, stir together all cheese mixture ingredients. Set aside.
4. To make sauce: In a large nonstick skillet sprayed with cooking spray, heat oil over medium-high heat; cook onions, garlic, and oregano for 5 minutes or until onions are browned. Stir in mushrooms; cook, stirring frequently, for 8 minutes or until mushrooms are browned and liquid is absorbed. Remove from heat. Stir in olives, sun-dried tomatoes, and feta cheese.
5. In a saucepan, whisk together stock, milk, flour, and mustard until flour is dissolved. Cook over medium-high heat, whisking, for 5 to 8 minutes or until thickened. Stir into mushroom mixture.
6. Arrange three noodles in bottom of baking dish. Top with one-third of mushroom sauce, then one-half of cheese mixture. Repeat layers. Top with remaining three noodles and remaining mushroom sauce. Sprinkle with Parmesan cheese. Cover pan tightly with foil.
7. Bake in centre of oven for 20 to 25 minutes or until hot.

super quick

PREP: About 10 mins.
COOK: About 10 mins.

MAKES 8 SERVINGS

MAKE AHEAD

Prepare salsa early in the day. Prepare pesto up to 3 days in advance. Freeze for up to 3 months. Combine salsa and pesto just after pasta is cooked, and then serve.

NUTRITIONAL ANALYSIS PER SERVING

294 calories

8 g protein

7.5 g fat, total

1.7 g fat, saturated

36 g carbohydrates

162 mg sodium

4.6 mg cholesterol

1.9 g fibre

TIPS

If the plum tomatoes are firm, there is no need to seed them. If they appear too ripe or watery, remove the seeds.

penne with creamy pesto and tomato salsa

Homemade pesto is delicious, easy to make, and contains fewer calories and less fat than the store-bought kind. I like to make it when basil is in season and freeze it in containers—it's a lot healthier for you than commercial pesto and less costly.

1 lb penne (cook pasta while preparing rest of dish)

PESTO

2 cups packed fresh basil leaves

2 tbsp grated Parmesan cheese

2 tbsp toasted pine nuts

1 tsp minced garlic

1/4 tsp salt

3 oz light cream cheese, softened

1/3 cup vegetable or chicken stock

2 tbsp olive oil

GARNISH

2 tbsp Parmesan cheese

TOMATO SALSA

2 cups diced plum tomatoes (about 12 oz)

1/3 cup diced sweet onions

2 tsp olive oil

2 tsp balsamic vinegar

1 tsp minced garlic

1/2 tsp dried basil

1/2 tsp hot pepper sauce

1. In a pot of boiling water, cook penne for 8 to 10 minutes or until tender but firm. Drain.
2. To make pesto: In a food processor, combine basil, Parmesan, pine nuts, garlic, and salt; process until finely chopped. Add cream cheese; process until well mixed. With motor running, add stock and oil through feed tube.
3. To make salsa: In a bowl, stir together all salsa ingredients.
4. Return pasta to saucepan. Pour pesto over pasta; toss to coat. Add tomato salsa; toss to coat. Garnish with Parmesan.

tortellini greek pasta salad in balsamic vinaigrette

 quick

PREP: About 15 mins.
COOK: About 10 mins.

MAKES 6 SERVINGS

MAKE AHEAD
Prepare dressing up to 2 days
ahead. Prepare pasta early in
the day and serve at room
temperature.

NUTRITIONAL ANALYSIS
PER SERVING
325 calories
14 g protein
12 g fat, total
4.6 g fat, saturated
38 g carbohydrates
438 mg sodium
33 mg cholesterol
1.6 g fibre

TIPS
Avoid buying meat tortellini,
since they contain more fat
and calories and often a
lower grade of meat. Rather
than buying anchovies in tins,
buy them in jars; opened jars
can be refrigerated.

I love the flavors of a Greek salad. Using its essential ingredients with tortellini pasta makes such a good dish! You don't need a large serving since these small, cheese-filled tortellini are quite filling; a large portion can add up in fat and calories. Serve this as a small side pasta dish along with some fish or chicken.

SALAD
1 lb fresh or frozen cheese tortellini (cook pasta while preparing rest of dish)
1 cup diced plum tomatoes
3/4 cup diced sweet green peppers
1/2 cup chopped green onions
1/4 cup sliced black olives
2 oz light feta cheese, crumbled

DRESSING
2 tbsp olive oil
1 tbsp balsamic vinegar
2 tbsp fresh lemon juice
1 tsp dried oregano
1 tsp minced garlic
2 anchovy fillets, minced
Freshly ground black pepper

GARNISH
3 tbsp chopped fresh oregano or parsley (optional)

1. To make salad: In a pot of boiling water, cook tortellini according to package directions. Drain. Rinse under cold running water; drain. In a large bowl, stir together tortellini and remaining salad ingredients.

2. To make dressing: In a small bowl, whisk together all dressing ingredients. Pour over tortellini mixture; toss to coat. Season to taste with pepper. Garnish salad with oregano (if using).

old-fashioned baked macaroni and cheese casserole

PREP: About 10 mins.
COOK: About 18 mins.

MAKES 8 SERVINGS

MAKE AHEAD
Prepare entire casserole and
freeze for up to 1 month or
refrigerate for 1 day before
baking. Bake for an extra
10 minutes if cold and thaw if
frozen before baking.

NUTRITIONAL ANALYSIS
PER SERVING
257 calories
14 g protein
4.5 g fat, total
2 g fat, saturated
40 g carbohydrates
600 mg sodium
8.4 mg cholesterol
1.3 g fibre

TIP
Feel free to add some diced
cooked chicken, shrimp, or
tofu to this recipe.

Great comfort food without the fat and calories, this macaroni and cheese is my children's favorite pasta dish. If your children prefer this to the boxed version, you know they have taste! I like to make a double recipe and freeze it in portion sizes for lunches or quick dinners.

12 oz elbow macaroni (2-1/2 cups) (cook pasta while preparing rest of dish)

SAUCE
1/4 cup all-purpose flour
1-1/2 cups chicken or vegetable stock
1-3/4 cups 2% milk
1-1/4 cups shredded low-fat Cheddar cheese
2 tbsp grated Parmesan cheese
1 tsp Dijon mustard
1/8 tsp each salt and freshly ground black pepper

TOPPING
1/3 cup dry seasoned bread crumbs
3 tbsp grated Parmesan cheese
1 tsp vegetable oil

1. In a large pot of boiling water, cook macaroni for 8 to 10 minutes or until tender but firm. Drain.
2. Preheat oven to 450°F. Spray an 8-cup casserole dish with cooking spray.
3. To make sauce: In a saucepan, whisk together flour, stock, and milk until smooth. Place over medium heat; cook, whisking, for 3 minutes, or until sauce is hot and thickened. Stir in cheeses, mustard, and salt and pepper; cook 1 minute longer, or until cheese melts. Remove from heat.
4. Toss pasta with cheese sauce. Pour into prepared casserole dish.
5. To make topping: In a small bowl, stir together all ingredients. Sprinkle over casserole.
6. Bake in centre of oven for 10 minutes or until golden.

caesar corn and red pepper risotto

This is an outstanding and unusual risotto dish. People always think risotto is difficult and time-consuming to make. On the contrary, it takes about 20 minutes and has a much richer flavor than regular rice. Most restaurants add excess butter and cheese to their risottos, resulting in a high fat and calorie content. In my version, I use a heart-healthy olive oil and a small amount of Parmesan cheese to give the flavor.

1 large sweet red pepper (roast pepper while preparing risotto)
1-3/4 cups drained canned corn

SAUCE	RICE
1 egg	4-1/2 to 5 cups chicken or vegetable stock
1/4 cup grated Parmesan cheese	2 tsp vegetable oil
3 tbsp olive oil	3/4 cup chopped onions
1 tbsp fresh lemon juice	1-1/2 tsp minced garlic
1 tsp minced garlic	1-1/2 cups Arborio rice
1/2 tsp Dijon mustard	1/2 cup chopped fresh parsley

1. Under a preheated broiler or over medium-high heat on a grill, cook pepper for 15 minutes, turning occasionally, or until charred on all sides. Cool. Peel, stem, core, and chop. Set aside.
2. In a nonstick skillet sprayed with cooking spray, sauté corn on medium heat for 8 minutes, stirring often, or until slightly charred. Set aside.
3. To make sauce: In a food processor, combine all sauce ingredients; purée until smooth.
4. To make rice: In a large saucepan, bring stock to a boil. Reduce heat to maintain a simmer. In a nonstick saucepan sprayed with cooking spray, heat oil over medium-high heat; cook onions and garlic for 5 minutes or until onion is softened. Stir in rice; cook, stirring, for 1 minute. Add 1/2 cup simmering stock; cook, stirring, until liquid is absorbed. Continue to cook, adding stock in 1/2 cup amounts, stirring constantly and making sure all liquid is absorbed before making next addition, for about 18 minutes or until rice is tender but slightly firm at the centre. Adjust heat as necessary to maintain slow bubbling simmer. Remove from heat.
5. Stir in parsley and reserved peppers and corn. Stir in sauce. Serve risotto immediately.

PREP: About 10 mins.
COOK: About 30 mins.

MAKES 6 SERVINGS

MAKE AHEAD
Grill pepper and sauté corn up to 2 days ahead. Grilled peppers can be frozen for up to 4 months. Prepare sauce up to 2 days ahead. Freeze for up to 1 month.

NUTRITIONAL ANALYSIS
PER SERVING
385 calories
13 g protein
13 g fat, total
2.6 g fat, saturated
54 g carbohydrates
467 mg sodium
39 mg cholesterol
3.5 g fibre

TIPS
If you don't want to roast a pepper, you can always use bottled roasted sweet red peppers (1 pepper is about 3 oz); make sure to use those packed in water, not oil. Freeze any remaining peppers either in plastic baggies or a container. Sautéing the corn gives it a delicious charred flavor.

tex mex risotto

PREP: About 10 mins.
COOK: About 28 mins.

MAKES 4 SERVINGS

MAKE AHEAD
Prepare sauce up to 1 day in
advance.

NUTRITIONAL ANALYSIS
PER SERVING
352 calories
10.1 g protein
4.4 g fat, total
1 g fat, saturated
68.7 g carbohydrates
383 mg sodium
3 mg cholesterol
4.8 g fibre

TIP
Canned corn, when sautéed
until browned, tastes like it is
just off the barbecue.

Southwest flavors have a significant presence in our restaurants and kitchens today. I like adding them to this traditional Italian dish. The simple combination of barbecue sauce and molasses in the sauce makes this a unique-tasting risotto.

SAUCE
1 cup chopped plum tomatoes
1/2 cup rinsed and drained canned black beans
2 tbsp barbecue sauce
2 tsp packed brown sugar
1-1/2 tsp cider vinegar
1-1/2 tsp molasses

RICE
3-1/2 cups chicken stock
2 tsp vegetable oil
1 cup chopped onions
2 tsp minced garlic
1 cup drained canned corn
1 cup Arborio rice

GARNISH
3 tbsp chopped fresh coriander or parsley

1. To make sauce: In a bowl, stir together all sauce ingredients. Set aside.
2. To make rice: In a saucepan, bring stock to a boil. Reduce heat to maintain a simmer. In a non-stick saucepan sprayed with cooking spray, heat oil over medium-high heat; cook onions and garlic for 5 minutes or until onion is softened. Stir in corn; cook for 5 to 8 minutes or just until corn begins to brown. Stir in rice; cook, stirring, for 1 minute. Add 1/2 cup simmering stock; cook, stirring, until liquid is absorbed. Continue to cook, adding stock in 1/2 cup amounts, stirring constantly and making sure all liquid is absorbed before making next addition, for about 18 minutes or until rice is tender but slightly firm in the centre. Adjust heat as necessary to maintain a slow bubbling simmer. Remove from heat.
3. Stir in sauce. Serve risotto immediately, sprinkled with coriander.

smoked salmon fettuccine alfredo

Everyone seems to love fettuccine Alfredo, also known as "heart attack on a plate"! I have created a recipe that not only is delicious and rich tasting, but also has a fraction of the fat and calories of the traditional.

12 oz fettuccine (cook pasta while preparing rest of dish)

SAUCE
1 cup cold fish or chicken stock
1 cup 2% evaporated milk
3 tbsp all-purpose flour
1 tsp Dijon mustard
1 tsp minced garlic
Pinch ground pepper

1/2 cup frozen green peas
6 tbsp grated Parmesan cheese
1/3 cup chopped fresh dill
6 oz smoked salmon, chopped

1. In a large pot of boiling water, cook fettuccine for 8 to 10 minutes or until tender but firm; drain.
2. To make sauce: In a large skillet, stir together all sauce ingredients until flour is dissolved. Cook over medium heat for 3 minutes, stirring, or just until thickened.
3. Stir in peas, half the Parmesan cheese, and half the dill. Add the sauce to the drained pasta; toss. Place on a serving platter. Garnish with remaining Parmesan, dill, and smoked salmon over top.

super quick

PREP: About 10 mins.
COOK: About 10 mins.

MAKES 6 SERVINGS

MAKE AHEAD
Make sauce up to 1 day ahead. Add extra stock when reheating if the sauce is too thick.

NUTRITIONAL ANALYSIS PER SERVING
339 calories
21 g protein
5.7 g fat, total
2.4 g fat, saturated
51.5 g carbohydrates
498 mg sodium
16 mg cholesterol
2.7 g fibre

TIP
Feel free to replace the smoked salmon with smoked trout or prosciutto.

shrimp goat cheese risotto

PREP: About 10 mins.
COOK: About 25 mins.

MAKES 4 SERVINGS

MAKE AHEAD
Sauté onion mixture early in
the day. Prepare risotto just
before serving.

NUTRITIONAL ANALYSIS
PER SERVING
376 calories
21.2 g protein
9.6 g fat, total
4.5 g fat, saturated
51.2 g carbohydrates
311 mg sodium
80 mg cholesterol
2 g fibre

Risotto is one of my favorite dishes when I dine Italian. Most risotto dishes are loaded with butter, oil, and cheese. My version calls for stronger tasting and lighter cheeses, which make for a healthier meal.

3-1/2 cups fish or chicken stock
2 tsp vegetable oil
1 cup chopped onions
2 tsp minced garlic
1 cup Arborio rice
6 oz deveined peeled shrimp, diced
2-1/2 oz goat cheese
2 tbsp grated Parmesan cheese
1/8 tsp freshly ground black pepper

GARNISH
1/3 cup chopped fresh basil

1. In a medium saucepan, bring stock to a boil. Reduce heat to maintain a simmer.
2. In a nonstick saucepan sprayed with cooking spray, heat oil over medium-high heat; cook onions and garlic for 5 minutes or until onions are softened. Stir in rice; cook, stirring, for 1 minute. Add 1/2 cup simmering stock; cook, stirring, until liquid is absorbed. Continue to cook, adding stock in 1/2 cup amounts, stirring constantly and making sure all liquid is absorbed before making next addition, for about 18 minutes or until rice is tender but slightly firm at the centre. Adjust heat as necessary to maintain a slow bubbling simmer. Stir in remaining ingredients, except basil; cook for 2 minutes longer or until shrimp is cooked through. Remove from heat. Serve sprinkled with basil.

pasta with chicken, garlic, and olives

I was inspired by this dish at a magnificent Ontario resort, the Muskoka Sands. The Boathouse Restaurant there serves a dish similar to this that is light and perfect for a hot summer's day. I adapted it and cut back on the oil. It's simple yet delicious.

12 oz boneless skinless chicken breast (about 3 breasts)

12 oz rotini (cook pasta while preparing rest of dish)

1/2 cup chopped plum tomatoes

1/2 cup chopped green onions

1/4 cup chopped fresh basil or parsley

1/4 cup sliced black olives

3 tbsp pine nuts

3 tbsp olive oil

2 tbsp fresh lemon juice

2 tbsp chicken stock or water

1 tbsp balsamic vinegar

1-1/2 tsp minced garlic

1 tsp Dijon mustard

1/8 tsp each salt and freshly ground black pepper

1. Preheat barbecue. On grill sprayed with cooking spray, cook chicken over medium-high heat for 6 minutes per side or until cooked through. (Alternatively, cook on a nonstick grill pan sprayed with cooking spray.) Slice thinly.

2. In a large pot of boiling water, cook rotini for 8 to 10 minutes or until tender but firm. Drain. Place in large bowl. Add chicken and remaining ingredients; toss to combine.

super quick

PREP: About 10 mins.
COOK: About 10 mins.

MAKES 6 SERVINGS

MAKE AHEAD
Grill chicken up to 1 day in advance.

NUTRITIONAL ANALYSIS PER SERVING
280 calories
14 g protein
11 g fat, total
1.4 g fat, saturated
30 g carbohydrates
124 mg sodium
12 mg cholesterol
1.3 g fibre

TIPS
To serve as a "salad" at room temperature, rinse pasta with cold water to stop cooking, and then add remaining ingredients. You can replace the chicken with cooked shrimp, pork, or beef.

PREP: About 15 mins.
COOK: About 10 mins.

MAKES 6 SERVINGS

MAKE AHEAD
Prepare sauce up to 4 days in advance. Freeze for up to 2 months. Do not stir-fry until ready to serve.

NUTRITIONAL ANALYSIS
PER SERVING
365 calories
22 g protein
4.6 g fat, total
0.7 g fat, saturated
59 g carbohydrates
403 mg sodium
33 mg cholesterol
2.3 g fibre

TIPS
This teriyaki sauce is a great one to double and keep in the refrigerator to use in pasta dishes or with cooked fish or chicken. It will keep for 2 weeks in the refrigerator. Use other vegetables such as broccoli, mushrooms, or sugar snap peas.

chicken teriyaki over rotini

My family could eat this dish every night of the week. Avoid bottled teriyaki sauces, which contain excess sodium and preservatives and never taste as good as the recipe below.

12 oz rotini (cook pasta while preparing rest of dish)

SAUCE
1/4 cup packed brown sugar
1/4 cup rice wine vinegar
1/4 cup water
1/4 cup low-sodium soy sauce
1 tbsp sesame oil
1 tbsp cornstarch
1-1/2 tsp minced garlic
1-1/2 tsp minced gingerroot

12 oz boneless skinless chicken breast (about 3 breasts), cubed
3 tbsp cornstarch
1 cup thinly sliced sweet red peppers
1 cup thinly sliced sweet yellow peppers
1 cup halved snow peas
2 tsp sesame seeds

GARNISH
1/4 cup fresh chopped coriander or parsley

1. In a large pot of boiling water, cook rotini for 8 to 10 minutes or until tender but firm; drain.
2. To make sauce: In a bowl, whisk together all sauce ingredients until smooth. Set aside.
3. Dust chicken cubes with cornstarch. In a wok or large nonstick skillet sprayed with cooking spray, cook chicken for 3 minutes over medium-high heat or until browned but not yet cooked through. Add peppers, snow peas, and sesame seeds; cook for 3 minutes or until chicken is just cooked through and vegetables are tender-crisp. Add sauce; cook for 2 minutes or until thickened and bubbly.
4. In a serving bowl, toss pasta with chicken-vegetable mixture. Serve immediately garnished with coriander.

chicken and sun-dried tomato cream sauce over penne

Sun-dried tomato sauce is always in my fridge or freezer. It's a great light sauce to use with pasta or over chicken or fish.

8 oz boneless skinless chicken breast (about 2 breasts), cut into 1-inch cubes

2 tbsp cornstarch

2 tsp vegetable oil

12 oz penne

SAUCE

1 cup 2% evaporated milk

1 cup chicken stock

3/4 cup chopped rehydrated sun-dried tomatoes

2 tbsp grated Parmesan cheese

1 tbsp tomato paste

2 tsp olive oil

2 tsp packed brown sugar

1-1/2 tsp minced garlic

GARNISH

1/4 cup chopped fresh basil

1 tbsp grated Parmesan cheese

1. Dust chicken with cornstarch. In a nonstick skillet sprayed with cooking spray, heat oil over medium-high heat; cook chicken for 3 minutes or until cooked through and browned on all sides. Do not overcook. Set pan aside.

2. In a large saucepan of boiling water, cook penne for 8 to 10 minutes or until tender but firm. Drain.

3. To make sauce: Process all sauce ingredients in a food processor until well combined. Pour sauce into pan with chicken. Add pasta. Cook over medium heat for 2 minutes or until pasta is hot. Serve sprinkled with basil and Parmesan.

PREP: About 10 mins.
COOK: About 10 mins.

MAKES 6 SERVINGS

MAKE AHEAD
Grill chicken up to 1 day in advance. Freeze cooked chicken breasts, wrapped individually, for up to 2 months. Prepare sauce up to 3 days in advance. Freeze for up to 2 months.

NUTRITIONAL ANALYSIS PER SERVING
385 calories
23.1 g protein
7.3 g fat, total
1.7 g fat, saturated
56.7 g carbohydrates
298 mg sodium
28 mg cholesterol
4.3 g fibre

TIPS
The key to keeping the chicken moist when you're not using excess oil is to dust it with cornstarch. This dish also goes well with large shrimp, scallops, or cubed pork or veal.

chicken tetrazzini with sun-dried tomatoes and feta cheese

PREP: About 20 mins.
COOK: About 25 mins.

MAKES 8 SERVINGS

MAKE AHEAD
Prepare casserole up to 1 day
in advance and refrigerate.
Bake cold casserole an extra
10 minutes. Alternatively,
freeze unbaked casserole for
up to 1 month. Thaw then
bake until warm.

NUTRITIONAL ANALYSIS
PER SERVING
340 calories
25 g protein
7 g fat, total
3.5 g fat, saturated
42 g carbohydrates
560 mg sodium
60 mg cholesterol
3 g fibre

TIP
It's fine to use leftover
chicken or turkey for this dish.

This is a recipe I created for the Mövenpick restaurants in Toronto. It's healthier than most tetrazzini gratin dishes, which usually are loaded with cheese and oil. Evaporated milk takes the place of heavy cream and gives the sauce a smooth texture.

12 oz penne (cook pasta while preparing
   rest of dish)
2 tsp oil
1-1/2 cups chopped onions
1-1/2 cups sliced mushrooms
1 cup chopped sweet green peppers
2 tsp minced garlic
1/2 tsp dried basil
1/8 tsp each salt and freshly ground
   black pepper
1-1/2 cups 2% evaporated milk
1-1/2 cups chicken stock

2 tbsp cornstarch, dissolved in about
   2 tbsp water
1 tsp Dijon mustard
8 oz cooked chicken breast (about 2 breasts),
   diced
3 oz light feta cheese, crumbled
1/3 cup chopped rehydrated sun-dried
   tomatoes
2 tbsp grated Parmesan cheese
1/4 cup chopped fresh parsley

TOPPING
1/2 cup shredded low-fat mozzarella cheese

1. Preheat oven to 425°F.
2. In a saucepan of boiling water, cook penne for 8 to 10 minutes or until tender but firm. Drain. Set aside.
3. In a nonstick saucepan, heat oil over medium-high heat; cook onions, mushrooms, peppers, and garlic for 10 minutes or until onions start to brown and other vegetables soften. Stir in basil and salt and pepper. Stir in milk, stock, dissolved cornstarch, and mustard; cook over medium heat for 3 minutes or just until thickened. Add chicken, feta, sun-dried tomatoes, Parmesan, parsley, and pasta. Put mixture into a 13- × 9-inch casserole dish. Sprinkle with mozzarella.
4. Bake in centre of oven for 10 minutes or until browned.

roasted peppers, olives, and prosciutto over rotini

What makes this pasta so delicious is the flavor of roasted vegetables. Using roasted peppers in their own juice along with a small amount of olive oil and lemon juice allows me to use half the amount of oil traditionally used in such a recipe.

1 head garlic

3 sweet peppers (various colors), halved, seeds and ribs removed

12 oz rotini

1/4 cup sliced black olives

2 oz prosciutto, chopped

3 tbsp grated Parmesan cheese

3 tbsp fresh lemon juice

2 tbsp olive oil

1 tbsp drained capers

1/8 tsp each salt and freshly ground black pepper

GARNISH
1/3 cup chopped fresh parsley

1. Preheat oven to 450°F. Spray baking sheet with cooking spray.
2. Cut 1/2-inch from top of head of garlic to expose cloves. Wrap garlic in foil. Place garlic and peppers on baking sheet. Roast in centre of oven for 25 minutes or until peppers are soft and blackened, turning once. Cool.
3. Meanwhile, in pot of boiling water, cook rotini for 8 to 10 minutes or until tender but firm; drain well and place in a serving bowl.
4. Peel peppers and slice. Squeeze garlic from skins. Add peppers and garlic to pasta along with remaining ingredients; toss to combine. Serve sprinkled with parsley.

PREP: About 10 mins.
COOK: About 25 mins.

MAKES 6 SERVINGS

MAKE AHEAD
Grill peppers and garlic up to 3 days before serving or freeze roasted peppers for up to 4 months.

NUTRITIONAL ANALYSIS PER SERVING
243 calories
8.6 g protein
11.6 g fat, total
3.1 g fat, saturated
26 g carbohydrates
363 mg sodium
10 mg cholesterol
3.2 g fibre

TIPS
A toaster oven is handy for roasting vegetables; grilling, however, will take less time. For a quick way to remove all the cloves of roasted garlic from the skin, squeeze the entire garlic from the base.

spaghetti with creamy tomato meat sauce and cheese topping

PREP: About 10 mins.
COOK: About 40 mins.

MAKES 8 SERVINGS

MAKE AHEAD
Prepare sauce up to 2 days in advance. Alternatively, prepare entire casserole and refrigerate for up to 2 days; if chilled, add 10 minutes to baking time.

NUTRITIONAL ANALYSIS
PER SERVING
372 calories
21 g protein
12 g fat, total
5.9 g fat, saturated
45 g carbohydrates
424 mg sodium
39 mg cholesterol
3 g fibre

TIPS
This is a great pasta dish to freeze in plastic containers for children's lunches. Instead of using beef, try a ground soy product, which is perfect for young vegetarians.

This is my new version of spaghetti and meat sauce. Adding ricotta cheese to the tomato sauce gives this traditional pasta dish a new twist.

2 tsp vegetable oil
1 cup chopped onions
1 tsp minced garlic
8 oz lean ground beef
2-1/2 cups tomato pasta sauce
1-1/2 tsp dried basil
1 tsp dried oregano
1/2 tsp hot pepper sauce
12 oz spaghetti (cook pasta while preparing rest of dish)

1-1/2 cups low-fat sour cream
1-1/2 cups light ricotta cheese
2 oz light cream cheese, softened
2 tbsp grated Parmesan cheese
Pinch each salt and freshly ground black pepper

TOPPING
1/2 cup shredded low-fat mozzarella cheese
2 tbsp grated Parmesan cheese

1. Preheat oven to 350°F. Spray a 13- × 9-inch glass baking dish with cooking spray.
2. In a nonstick saucepan, heat oil over medium heat; cook onions and garlic for 5 minutes or until softened. Stir in beef; cook for 5 minutes, or until no longer pink, stirring to break up meat. Stir in tomato sauce, basil, oregano, and hot pepper sauce. Reduce heat to a simmer; cook for 10 minutes, covered.
3. Meanwhile, in pot of boiling water, cook spaghetti for 8 to 10 minutes or until tender but firm; drain. In a food processor, combine sour cream, cheeses, and salt and pepper; purée until smooth.
4. Place drained spaghetti in baking dish. Spoon sour cream mixture on top of spaghetti, mixing well. Spoon tomato sauce evenly over top. Mix together topping ingredients; sprinkle over casserole.
5. Bake in centre of oven for 20 minutes. Spoon out to serve.

creamy baked beefaroni

This is a recipe I created for *Rose Reisman's Enlightened Home Cooking*. It has become a weekly staple in our home and sure beats the boxed or canned version! Lately I've been substituting ground soy for the ground beef, which means that more soy protein gets into my family's diet. The soy version is also great for vegetarians or for people who keep kosher.

1 lb penne (cook pasta while preparing dish)

MEAT SAUCE	CHEESE SAUCE
1 tsp vegetable oil	1/4 cup all-purpose flour
1 cup chopped onions	2 cups 2% milk
2 tsp minced garlic	1-1/2 cups beef or chicken stock
12 oz lean ground beef	1 cup shredded low-fat Cheddar cheese
1-3/4 cups tomato pasta sauce	
1/2 cup beef or chicken stock	

TOPPING

1/2 cup shredded low-fat mozzarella cheese

2 tbsp grated Parmesan cheese

1. Preheat oven to 450°F. Spray a 13- × 9-inch glass baking dish with cooking spray.
2. In a large pot of boiling water, cook penne for 8 to 10 minutes or until tender but firm. Drain.
3. To make meat sauce: In a nonstick saucepan, heat oil over medium heat; cook onions and garlic for 4 minutes or until softened. Stir in beef; cook, stirring to break up meat, for 4 minutes, or until no longer pink. Stir in tomato sauce and stock. Cover and cook for 10 minutes or until thickened. Set aside.
4. To make cheese sauce: In a nonstick saucepan, whisk together flour, milk, and stock until flour dissolves. Place over medium heat; simmer until mixture begins to boil. Reduce heat to low; cook, stirring occasionally, for 5 minutes, or until thickened. Stir in Cheddar. Remove from heat. Stir cheese sauce into meat sauce.
5. Toss pasta with sauce. Pour into prepared baking dish. Sprinkle with mozzarella and Parmesan.
6. Bake in centre of oven for 10 minutes or until bubbly.

PREP: About 15 mins.
COOK: About 35 mins.

MAKES 10 SERVINGS

MAKE AHEAD
Prepare uncooked casserole and freeze for up to 2 months or bake and freeze up to 1 month. It can be prepared 2 days in advance and then baked. If frozen, thaw then bake.

NUTRITIONAL ANALYSIS PER SERVING
338 calories
21 g protein
8.7 g fat, total
3.3 g fat, saturated
44 g carbohydrates
507 mg sodium
21 mg cholesterol
2.5 g fibre

TIPS
I usually double this recipe and freeze some in portions for my children's lunches or dinners. It keeps for 2 months in the freezer.

rice and beef tagine with spinach and dried fruits

PREP: About 10 mins.
COOK: About 40 mins.

MAKES 6 SERVINGS

MAKE AHEAD
Cook rice early in the day.
Prepare filling up to 1 day
in advance.

NUTRITIONAL ANALYSIS
PER SERVING
470 calories
23.5 g protein
11.5 g fat, total
3.6 g fat, saturated
75 g carbohydrates
108 mg sodium
29 mg cholesterol
4.3 g fibre

TIPS
For a no-fuss preparation, you
can use a rice cooker with a
warming feature. Substitute
ground chicken, veal, or pork
for the beef.

A tagine is a North African dish often made with vegetables, fish, chicken, veal, and dried fruits. The deep, glazed-earthenware dish with a conical lid in which the food is baked gives it its name. My tagine, cooked right on top of the stove in a common skillet, combines lean ground beef, spinach, and dried fruits. It has a wonderful, savory taste.

2 cups basmati or jasmine rice (cook rice while preparing rest of dish)
2-1/2 cups chicken or beef stock
1/4 cup chopped fresh coriander or parsley
2 tsp olive oil
2 tsp vegetable oil
1-1/2 cups chopped onions
2 tsp minced garlic
1 lb extra lean ground beef
1/2 cup cooked drained spinach

1/3 cup chopped dried apricots
1/3 cup chopped dried dates
2 tsp fresh lemon juice
1 tsp paprika
1/2 tsp cinnamon
1/4 tsp ginger
1/4 tsp freshly ground black pepper

GARNISH
1/4 cup chopped fresh coriander or parsley

1. In a large saucepan, combine rice and stock. Bring to a boil. Reduce heat to a simmer; cover and cook for 10 minutes. Remove from heat and let stand, covered, for 10 minutes. Stir in coriander and olive oil.

2. In a large nonstick skillet sprayed with cooking spray, heat vegetable oil over medium-high heat; cook onions and garlic for 5 minutes or until golden. Add beef; cook for 5 minutes or until no longer pink, stirring to break up meat. Add remaining ingredients except coriander; cook for 1 minute. Remove from pan. Wipe pan clean and spray with cooking spray. Add half the rice mixture to the pan; press firmly with a spatula sprayed with cooking spray. Add beef mixture, patting it down. Add remaining rice, patting it down. Cover pan and cook on low heat for 20 minutes or until heated through and bottom of rice becomes crunchy.

3. Serve from pan, garnished with coriander.

meat

PREP: About 5 mins.
COOK: About 12 mins.

MAKES 4 SERVINGS

MAKE AHEAD
Prepare sauce up to 1 week
in advance. Sauté veal early
in the day and refrigerate.
Bake another 10 minutes if
chilled. Freeze for up to
2 months.

NUTRITIONAL ANALYSIS
PER SERVING
215 calories
17 g protein
11 g fat, total
3 g fat, saturated
12 g carbohydrates
433 mg sodium
43 mg cholesterol
0.8 g fibre

TIPS
If you can't find low-sodium
soy sauce, make your own by
diluting regular soy sauce
with the same amount of
water. If the veal chops are
thinner than 1 inch, bake for
only 5 minutes.

hoisin veal chops

If you want leaner meat, select rib or loin veal chops, which both contain only 7 grams of fat per 3-1/2 ounce serving. A veal chop is leaner than a beef steak. The Asian flavor of the hoisin-orange-peanut sauce goes beautifully with the meat. Leaving the bone in gives the meat more tenderness.

SAUCE
1/4 cup hoisin sauce
2 tbsp orange juice concentrate, thawed
1 tbsp rice wine vinegar
1 tbsp low-sodium soy sauce
1 tbsp natural peanut butter
1 tsp sesame oil
1 tsp minced garlic
1/2 tsp minced gingerroot

CHOPS
1 lb bone-in veal rib chops, 1-inch thick
2 tbsp all-purpose flour

GARNISH
3 tbsp chopped fresh coriander or parsley

1. Preheat oven to 400°F.
2. To make sauce: In a food processor or in a bowl using a whisk, mix sauce ingredients together.
3. Dust chops with flour. In a nonstick skillet sprayed with cooking spray, cook chops on medium-high heat for 2 minutes per side or until browned. Transfer to a shallow baking dish. Pour half the sauce over.
4. Bake uncovered in centre of oven for about 10 minutes or until just cooked through. Do not overcook. Gently heat remaining sauce, serve with veal and garnish with parsley.

calves' liver with caramelized onions

Calves' liver is one of the most tender veal cuts available. It melts in your mouth. Beef liver is tougher and harder to digest. More delicate and milder in flavor than beef liver, calves' liver is outstanding with caramelized onions.

2 tsp vegetable oil
4 cups sliced sweet onions
2 tbsp packed brown sugar
1-1/2 tsp minced garlic
1-1/2 lb calves' liver

GARNISH
1/4 cup chopped fresh parsley

1. In a large nonstick skillet sprayed with cooking spray, heat oil over medium heat; cook onions for 8 minutes or until softened. Stir in sugar and garlic. Reduce heat to low; cook for 15 minutes, stirring occasionally, or until onions are browned.
2. Meanwhile, either on the grill of a preheated barbecue or in a nonstick grill pan sprayed with cooking spray, cook liver until medium done, about 5 minutes or to your liking. Place on a serving platter and spoon onions over top. Serve garnished with parsley.

PREP: About 5 mins.
COOK: About 25 mins.

MAKES 6 SERVINGS

MAKE AHEAD
Prepare onions up to 2 days in advance; keep refrigerated. Freeze for up to 6 weeks.

NUTRITIONAL ANALYSIS
PER SERVING
220 calories
21.7 g protein
6.7 g fat, total
2 g fat, saturated
18.2 g carbohydrates
76 mg sodium
350 mg cholesterol
2.2 g fibre

TIPS
Calves' liver should be pale red to yellow-brown in color, unlike the reddish brown of beef liver. Be sure to buy the sweetest onions, such as Vidalia, Walla Walla, or Maui.

PREP: About 10 mins.
COOK: About 12 mins.

MAKES 4 SERVINGS

MAKE AHEAD
Prepare sauce and sauté
mushrooms up to 1 day in
advance, keeping them separate. Heat together gently just
before serving. Freeze for up
to 4 weeks.

NUTRITIONAL ANALYSIS
PER SERVING
300 calories
37.1 g protein
12 g fat, total
4 g fat, saturated
8.7 g carbohydrates
181 mg sodium
97.8 mg cholesterol
1.4 g fibre

TIPS
Oyster mushrooms have little
moisture and a meaty texture,
making them a great mush-
room to cook with. Feel free
to use other mushroom varieties, but be sure to cook
them on medium-high heat to
rid them of excess moisture.

beef tenderloin with mushroom sauce

Beef tenderloin is one of the leanest beef cuts. A 3 ounce serving contains 189 calories and 10 grams of fat compared to a rib-eye roast, which has more than 300 calories and 18 grams of fat for a serving of the same size. This tenderloin with a sweet and savory mushroom sauce is wonderful. I often buy a whole tenderloin and roast it. I like to sear it first in a nonstick skillet, then bake it at 425°F. Cooking it rare will take about 15 to 20 minutes per pound.

1 tsp vegetable oil
1 cup thinly sliced oyster mushrooms
1/3 cup diced red onions
1 tsp minced garlic

SAUCE
1/2 cup 2% evaporated milk
1/3 cup beef stock
1 tbsp all-purpose flour
1 tbsp balsamic vinegar
1/2 tsp Dijon mustard
1/8 tsp each salt and freshly ground black pepper

4 beef tenderloin steaks (4 oz each)

GARNISH
1/4 cup chopped fresh parsley

1. In a nonstick skillet sprayed with cooking spray, heat oil over medium-high heat; cook mush-rooms, onions, and garlic for 6 minutes, stirring occasionally, or until golden. Set aside.
2. To make sauce: In a small nonstick skillet, mix sauce ingredients until smooth, then cook on medium heat, stirring frequently, for 3 minutes or until bubbly and thickened.
3. Preheat barbecue. On grill sprayed with cooking spray, cook beef over medium-high heat for 3 to 5 minutes per side or until desired doneness. (Alternatively, cook in a nonstick grill pan over medium-high heat.)
4. Stir mushrooms into sauce. Serve spooned over beef, sprinkled with parsley.

flank steak with maple syrup and orange marinade over sweet potatoes

If I want to eat meat frequently, I often make flank steak. Having no excess fat, it is one of the leanest cuts of beef. You must marinate it, though, for at least two hours and preferably longer to obtain the most tender texture. Also, be sure to cut flank steak across the grain when slicing.

MARINADE

1/3 cup maple syrup

1/3 cup orange juice concentrate, thawed

1/3 cup beef or chicken stock

3 tbsp balsamic vinegar

1 tbsp liquid honey

1-1/2 tsp minced garlic

1 tsp Dijon mustard

SAUCE

2 tsp cornstarch

reserved marinade

1-1/2 lb flank steak

SWEET POTATOES

2 lb sweet potatoes, peeled and cubed (about 8 cups) (boil potatoes while cooking steak)

1/4 cup chopped green onions

2 tbsp liquid honey

1 tbsp olive oil

GARNISH

1/4 cup chopped fresh parsley, as garnish

PREP: Marinate steak 2 h or overnight
COOK: About 15 mins.

MAKES 6 SERVINGS

MAKE AHEAD
Prepare marinade up to 1 week in advance. Prepare the potatoes up to 1 day in advance, reheating gently when ready to serve. Freeze for up to 6 weeks.

NUTRITIONAL ANALYSIS PER SERVING
450 calories
28 g protein
13 g fat, total
4 g fat, saturated
63.6 g carbohydrates
133 mg sodium
80.5 mg cholesterol
5.1 g fibre

TIP
To save time, prepare the sweet potatoes, which can be reheated later, while the meat is marinating.

1. To make marinade: In a 13- × 9-inch glass baking dish, stir together all marinade ingredients. Add flank steak; turn to coat. Cover with plastic wrap. Marinate in refrigerator for at least 2 hours, turning occasionally. (Marinate overnight for a more tender texture.)

2. Preheat barbecue.

3. To make sweet potatoes: Place potatoes in a saucepan; add cold water to cover. Bring to a boil. Cover, reduce heat to medium-high, and boil for 10 minutes or until potatoes are soft. Drain. Return to pan; mash. Stir in green onions, honey, and olive oil. Cover to keep warm.

4. Reserving marinade, place steak on greased grill; cook over medium-high heat for 8 minutes, turning halfway, or until medium-rare. (Alternatively, cook in a nonstick grill pan over medium-high heat for the same time.) Cover with foil; let stand for 10 minutes.

5. To make sauce: Meanwhile, place reserved marinade in a small saucepan with the cornstarch; stir until dissolved. Bring to a boil. Reduce heat to medium; and simmer for 5 minutes.

6. Place sweet potatoes on a serving platter. Slice steak against the grain; arrange over sweet potatoes. Pour sauce over and serve garnished with parsley.

flank steak in black bean sauce with bok choy

Black bean sauce goes well with a tender flank steak. To make it tender, marinating the steak is a must. The small bok choy available is sweeter tasting than the larger green one.

BLACK BEAN MARINADE

1/2 cup packed brown sugar

1/2 cup ketchup

1/3 cup black bean sauce

1/3 cup beef or chicken stock

2 tbsp rice wine vinegar

4 tsp sesame oil

2 tsp minced garlic

2 tsp minced gingerroot

1-1/2 lb flank steak

4 cup chopped bok choy

2 tsp sesame oil

GARNISH

1/4 cup chopped fresh coriander

1. To make marinade: In a 13- × 9-inch glass baking dish, stir together all marinade ingredients. Add flank steak; turn to coat. Cover with plastic wrap. Marinate in refrigerator for at least 2 hours, turning occasionally. (Marinate overnight for a more tender texture.)
2. Preheat barbecue.
3. Reserving marinade, place steak on greased grill; cook over medium-high heat for 8 minutes, turning halfway, or until medium-rare. (Alternatively, cook in a nonstick grill pan over medium-high heat for the same time.) Cover with foil; let stand for 10 minutes. Meanwhile, place reserved marinade in a small saucepan; bring to a boil. Reduce heat to medium; simmer for 5 minutes.
4. In a nonstick skillet sprayed with cooking spray, cook bok choy on medium-high heat for 3 minutes or until it starts to wilt. Stir in sesame oil and transfer to a platter.
5. Slice steak against the grain. Arrange over bok choy. Pour sauce over and serve garnished with coriander.

PREP: Marinate steak 2 h or overnight
COOK: About 15 mins.

MAKES 6 SERVINGS

MAKE AHEAD
Prepare marinade up to 1 week in advance. Freeze for up to 6 weeks.

NUTRITIONAL ANALYSIS PER SERVING
390 calories
26 g protein
13 g fat, total
4 g fat, saturated
27 g carbohydrates
458 mg sodium
81 mg cholesterol
1.2 g fibre

TIP
If you want a side dish, serve with chow mein noodles and extra sauce.

thai ginger meatballs in coconut sauce

You've never tried meatballs like these before! Forget spaghetti and meatballs. Thai flavors have taken over. These are beautiful to serve as an appetizer or main dish over rice noodles, rice, or couscous.

SAUCE

3/4 cup light coconut milk

1/3 cup beef or chicken stock

2 tsp fresh lemon juice

2 tsp fish sauce or hoisin sauce

2 tsp packed brown sugar

1 tsp cornstarch

1 tsp minced gingerroot

1 tsp minced garlic

MEATBALLS

1 lb extra lean ground beef

1 egg

1/4 cup hoisin sauce

1/4 cup finely diced green onions

3 tbsp dry unseasoned bread crumbs

2 tbsp finely chopped fresh coriander

2 tsp minced garlic

1-1/2 tsp crushed gingerroot

1/8 tsp each salt and freshly ground black pepper

GARNISH

2 tbsp chopped fresh coriander

1. To make sauce: In a bowl, stir together sauce ingredients until cornstarch is dissolved.
2. To make meatballs: In a bowl, stir together meatball ingredients. Form into 1-inch meatballs, making about 30.
3. In a large nonstick skillet sprayed with cooking spray, cook meatballs on medium-high heat for 5 minutes, turning occasionally, or until browned. Add sauce. Reduce heat to a simmer, cover, and cook for 15 minutes, stirring occasionally, or until meatballs are cooked through and sauce is slightly thickened. Serve garnished with coriander.

PREP: About 20 mins.
COOK: About 20 mins.

MAKES 4 SERVINGS

MAKE AHEAD
This dish can be made 1 day in advance and gently heated before serving. Freeze portions in sauce for up to 2 months.

NUTRITIONAL ANALYSIS PER SERVING
295 calories
27.1 g protein
12 g fat, total
6 g fat, saturated
17 g carbohydrates
420 mg sodium
95 mg cholesterol
1.3 g fibre

TIPS
Light coconut milk, which can be found in supermarkets, contains 75 percent less fat, calories, and cholesterol than regular coconut milk. Fish sauce, once cooked, gives food a wonderful flavor. If using hoisin sauce, you may want to reduce the amount of sugar in the sauce slightly.

PREP: About 5 mins.
COOK: About 18 mins.

MAKES 4 SERVINGS

MAKE AHEAD
Prepare sauce up to 1 week
in advance. Sauté tenderloin
up to 1 day in advance.
Freeze for up to 2 months.

NUTRITIONAL ANALYSIS
PER SERVING
187 calories
16 g protein
3 g fat, total
1 g fat, saturated
24 g carbohydrates
82 mg sodium
45 mg cholesterol
0.5 g fibre

TIPS
The baking time can vary
greatly depending on the
thickness of the tenderloin. If
you are uncertain about the
baking time, it's best to use a
meat thermometer. Feel free
to substitute veal or beef tenderloin for the pork. You can
always grill the tenderloin
instead of baking it.

pork tenderloin with apricot maple syrup glaze

Pork contains half the fat of beef tenderloin. A 3-1/2 ounce serving of pork contains only 5 grams of fat. It is a delicious cut of meat but will dry out if overcooked. The combination of apricot jam, maple syrup, and diced dried apricots makes this an outstanding dinner.

1/4 cup apricot jam
1/4 cup maple syrup
1/4 cup cider vinegar
2 tsp Dijon mustard

1 lb pork tenderloin, 2-inch thick (you may need 2 tenderloins)

GARNISH
1/3 cup diced dried apricots
3 tbsp chopped green onions
3 tbsp fresh chopped coriander or parsley

1. Preheat oven to 425°F.
2. In a bowl, whisk together apricot jam, maple syrup, vinegar, and mustard.
3. In a nonstick grill pan sprayed with cooking spray, cook tenderloin on medium-high heat for 3 minutes, turning occasionally, or until browned on all sides. Transfer to a shallow baking dish. Brush one-quarter of glaze over tenderloin. Bake for 15 to 20 minutes just until medium cooked, or until the temperature on a meat thermometer reaches about 155°F.
4. Gently heat remaining glaze. Sprinkle meat with apricots, green onions, and coriander. Serve with remaining glaze.

pesto- and feta-crusted rack of lamb

I always consider rack of lamb a treat and a delicacy. Lamb is higher in fat and calories than most meats but well worth the indulgence. Be sure to trim away any excess fat and not to over-cook the lamb. This version, with a pesto and feta cheese topping, is over the top!

To achieve the best results, I highly recommend using an electronic meat thermometer. The one I use has a prong that goes into the meat and a wire that extends from the prong out the oven door to a temperature gauge that you keep on the counter. You never have to open the oven.

1-1/2 lb to 2 lb rack of lamb (2 racks with about 7 ribs each)
2 tbsp Rose's Light Pesto (see page 184) or store-bought
1 oz light feta cheese, crumbled
2 tbsp dry seasoned bread crumbs

GARNISH
1/4 cup chopped fresh parsley

1. Preheat oven to 425°F. Spray baking sheet with cooking spray.
2. In a nonstick skillet sprayed with cooking spray, cook lamb on medium-high heat for 5 minutes, turning occasionally, or until browned. Place bone side down on baking sheet.
3. In a small bowl, combine pesto and feta cheese. Spread over meaty part of lamb. Roast in centre of oven for 10 minutes. Remove from oven.
4. Pat bread crumbs over lamb. Return to oven. Roast to medium-rare, about another 10 minutes, or until the temperature on a meat thermometer reaches 150°F. Let rest for 10 minutes before slicing between the bones. Serve garnished with parsley.

PREP: About 5 mins.
COOK: About 25 mins.

MAKES 6 SERVINGS

MAKE AHEAD
Step 2 can be done early in the day. Freeze for up to 6 weeks.

NUTRITIONAL ANALYSIS PER SERVING
380 calories
24 g protein
20 g fat, total
10 g fat, saturated
2.5 g carbohydrates
205 mg sodium
98 mg cholesterol
0.3 g fibre

chicken and turkey

chicken roll-ups with asparagus and cheese

PREP: About 15 mins.
COOK: About 18 mins.

MAKES 4 SERVINGS

MAKE AHEAD
Prepare breaded chicken rolls
up to 1 day in advance. Bake
just before serving, adding
10 minutes to baking time if
dish is chilled. Freeze for up
to 6 weeks.

NUTRITIONAL ANALYSIS
PER SERVING
303 calories
35 g protein
7.9 g fat, total
2.5 g fat, saturated
23 g carbohydrates
425 mg sodium
127 mg cholesterol
1.3 g fibre

TIPS
Be sure to rinse cooked
asparagus in cold water until
stalks are no longer warm, or
they will turn brown instead
of staying bright green. Your
butcher will be happy to
pound the chicken breasts if
you don't want to bother. The
thinner the breasts, the easier
they are to roll.

Rolled chicken breasts with various fillings are easy to make and look great. This dish has the contrasting colors of green asparagus, white cheese, and browned chicken breasts. I like to serve it cut into medallions, or sliced in half to expose the colorful interior.

4 spears asparagus
2 oz light mozzarella or Havarti cheese
4 boneless skinless chicken breasts (about 1 lb total)
1 egg
2 tbsp water
3/4 cup dry seasoned bread crumbs
2 tbsp chopped fresh parsley
2 tsp vegetable oil

1. Preheat oven to 425°F. Spray rimmed baking sheet with vegetable spray.
2. Trim woody thick ends from asparagus, leaving about 3 inches at the tip end. In a large pot of boiling water, cook asparagus tips for 2 minutes or until tender-crisp. Drain. Rinse under cold running water. Drain. Break asparagus in half.
3. Cut cheese into 4 equal logs.
4. Between 2 sheets of waxed paper, pound chicken breasts to an even 1/2-inch thickness. Place 1 asparagus spear and 1 piece of cheese crosswise on breast near end. Roll up. Secure edges with a toothpick or small skewer. Repeat with remaining breasts.
5. In a shallow bowl, beat egg with water. On a separate plate, stir together bread crumbs and parsley.
6. In a large nonstick skillet sprayed with cooking spray, heat oil over medium-high heat. Dip each chicken breast in the egg mixture; coat each with the bread crumbs mixture. Cook for 3 minutes, turning occasionally, or until well browned on all sides. Transfer to a baking sheet. Bake in centre of oven for 10 minutes or until chicken is cooked through.
7. Remove toothpicks before serving. Serve whole or slice crosswise into medallions.

chicken breasts stuffed with brie, red peppers, and green onions

People are shocked when they see Brie in a low-fat recipe. But remember, it's all about moderation! This dish, with its wonderful color and texture, is beautiful and delicious.

2 oz Brie, at room temperature

3 tbsp finely chopped sweet red peppers

3 tbsp finely chopped green onions

1 tsp minced garlic

1 egg

2 tbsp low-fat milk

1/2 cup dry seasoned bread crumbs

4 boneless skinless chicken breasts (about 1 lb total)

1 tbsp vegetable oil

1. Preheat oven to 425°F. Spray rimmed baking sheet with cooking spray.
2. In a small bowl, mix Brie, peppers, green onions, and garlic. In a shallow bowl, whisk together egg and milk. Place bread crumbs on a plate.
3. Between 2 sheets of waxed paper, pound chicken breasts to an even 1/2-inch thickness. Put 1 tbsp of the Brie mixture at the short end of each chicken breast. Roll up tightly. Secure edge with a toothpick or small skewer.
4. In a large nonstick skillet sprayed with cooking spray, heat oil over medium-high heat. Dip each chicken roll in the egg mixture; coat each with bread crumbs. Cook for 3 minutes, turning often, or until browned on all sides. Transfer to prepared baking sheet. Bake in centre of oven for 10 minutes or until chicken is cooked through. Remove toothpicks before serving. Serve whole or cut chicken crosswise into medallions.

PREP: About 15 mins.
COOK: About 15 mins.

MAKES 4 SERVINGS

MAKE AHEAD
Prepare stuffed and sautéed chicken rolls up to 1 day in advance. Bake just before serving, adding 10 minutes to baking time if dish is chilled. Freeze for up to 6 weeks.

NUTRITIONAL ANALYSIS PER SERVING
279 calories
33 g protein
11 g fat, total
3.6 g fat, saturated
12 g carbohydrates
320 mg sodium
134 mg cholesterol
0.9 g fibre

TIPS
You can use roasted sweet red peppers packed in water for a sweeter flavor. You can also use another cheese of your choice. Some of my favorites are feta or goat cheese.

chicken with apricot glaze

PREP: About 10 mins.
COOK: About 30 mins.

MAKES 6 SERVINGS

MAKE AHEAD
Prepare entire dish up to
1 day in advance. Bake just
before serving, adding
10 minutes to baking time if
dish is chilled. Freeze for up
to 6 weeks.

NUTRITIONAL ANALYSIS
PER SERVING
410 calories
33 g protein
11 g fat, total
3 g fat, saturated
26 g carbohydrates
290 mg sodium
100 mg cholesterol
0.1 g fibre

TIPS
Before eating the chicken,
remember to remove the skin
since it contains a lot of the
fat and calories. The skin on a
piece of chicken can add
more than 8 grams of fat!

Initially I created this glaze for a whole roasted chicken stuffed with couscous. The glaze was so delicious I thought it would be wonderful over pieces of chicken. This chicken can be served over steamed rice or a bed of couscous.

GLAZE
1/2 cup apricot jam
1/4 cup sweet chili sauce
2 tbsp water
1 tbsp low-sodium soy sauce
1 tbsp liquid honey
1 tsp minced garlic
1 tsp minced gingerroot

CHICKEN
2 chicken breasts, skin-on, bone-in (about 1-1/2 lb total)
2 chicken legs, skin-on, bone-in (about 1-1/4 lb total)
3 tbsp all-purpose flour
2 tsp vegetable oil

GARNISH
3 tbsp chopped fresh parsley

1. Preheat oven to 400°F. Spray rimmed baking sheet with cooking spray.
2. To make glaze: In a bowl, whisk glaze ingredients together until smooth.
3. To make chicken: Dust chicken with flour. In a nonstick skillet sprayed with cooking spray, heat oil over medium heat. Cook chicken in batches until browned on all sides, about 5 minutes. Transfer to prepared baking sheet. Pour half of apricot mixture over top.
4. Bake in centre of oven for 25 to 30 minutes or until chicken is cooked through. Gently heat remaining glaze. Garnish with parsley and serve with remaining glaze.

chicken with creamy dijon cheese sauce

This is a wonderful chicken dish to serve with a large salad and some cooked asparagus or broccoli. The low-fat evaporated milk gives the sauce a creamy texture similar to cream but without the fat and calories. I like to use 1% or 2% evaporated milk. Avoid using skim evaporated milk since it has a watery consistency.

4 boneless skinless chicken breasts (about 1 lb total)
2 tbsp all-purpose flour
2 tsp vegetable oil

SAUCE
1 cup 2% evaporated milk
1-1/2 tsp all-purpose flour
1 tsp Dijon mustard
1/4 cup shredded light Cheddar cheese
2 tbsp grated Parmesan cheese

TOPPING
2 tbsp dry seasoned bread crumbs
1 tbsp grated Parmesan cheese
1-1/2 tsp water
1/8 tsp freshly ground black pepper

GARNISH
2 tbsp finely chopped fresh parsley

1. Preheat broiler. Spray rimmed baking sheet with cooking spray.
2. Between 2 sheets of waxed paper, pound chicken breasts to an even 1/2-inch thickness. Dust chicken with flour. In a large nonstick skillet, heat oil over medium-high heat. Cook chicken for 5 minutes or until cooked through and browned on both sides. Transfer to prepared baking sheet.
3. To make sauce: In a small saucepan, whisk together evaporated milk, flour, and mustard. Cook over medium heat for 3 minutes or until hot and slightly thickened. Remove from heat. Whisk in Cheddar and Parmesan.
4. To make topping: In a bowl, stir together topping ingredients.
5. Pour sauce over chicken. Sprinkle with topping. Broil for 1 to 2 minutes or until topping is browned. Garnish with parsley.

super quick

PREP: About 10 mins.
COOK: About 10 mins.

MAKES 4 SERVINGS

MAKE AHEAD
Bread chicken and prepare sauce up to 1 day in advance. Cook sauce and chicken, and freeze dish for up to 1 month.

NUTRITIONAL ANALYSIS PER SERVING
260 calories
35 g protein
7.1 g fat, total
3.1 g fat, saturated
13 g carbohydrates
405 mg sodium
81 mg cholesterol
0.3 g fibre

TIPS
If you make the sauce ahead of time, when reheating it you'll need to add either extra evaporated milk or some stock. If the chicken was prepared ahead of time, it's best to warm it in a 425°F oven instead of broiling.

chicken with avocado tomato salsa

PREP: About 15 mins.
COOK: About 5 mins.

MAKES 4 SERVINGS

MAKE AHEAD
Prepare salsa a few hours
in advance.

NUTRITIONAL ANALYSIS
PER SERVING
255 calories
27.3 g protein
10.6 g fat, total
1.7 g fat, saturated
12.5 g carbohydrates
96 mg sodium
65.8 mg cholesterol
2.7 g fibre

TIP
A student gave me a great tip
to prevent avocados from
going brown. Before cutting
the avocado and without
piercing it, heat on High in a
microwave for 30 seconds. It
truly works!

I love to serve this chicken in the summer outdoors or at a Sunday brunch. The salsa is fresh tasting, and the contrasting colors are beautiful.

4 boneless skinless chicken breasts (about 1 lb total)
3 tbsp cornstarch
3 tsp vegetable oil

SALSA
1 cup chopped plum tomatoes
1/2 cup diced avocado
3 tbsp chopped fresh coriander
1 tbsp olive oil
2 tsp fresh lime or lemon juice
1 tsp minced garlic
1/2 tsp liquid honey
1/2 tsp hot sauce

1. Between 2 sheets of waxed paper, pound chicken breasts to an even 1/2-inch thickness. Dust chicken with cornstarch. In a nonstick skillet sprayed with cooking spray, heat oil over medium-high heat. Cook chicken for 5 to 8 minutes, turning once, or until cooked through. Place on serving dish.

2. To make salsa: In a bowl, stir together salsa ingredients.

3. Spoon salsa over chicken before serving.

chicken parmesan with sun-dried tomatoes

The combination of sun-dried tomatoes with sweet peppers and tomato sauce is delicious over boneless chicken breasts. I buy sun-dried tomatoes in bulk and use as needed. Just pour boiling water over them and let sit for 15 minutes. Drain, and then chop.

4 tsp vegetable oil
1 cup chopped onions
1 tsp minced garlic
1 cup chopped sweet red or green peppers
1/3 cup chopped rehydrated sun-dried
   tomatoes
1 cup tomato pasta sauce
1/2 cup chicken stock
1 tsp dried basil
1/2 tsp dried oregano
4 boneless skinless chicken breasts
   (about 1 lb total)

1 egg
2 tbsp water
3/4 cup dry seasoned bread crumbs
1 tbsp grated Parmesan cheese

TOPPING
1/3 cup shredded light mozzarella cheese
1 tbsp grated Parmesan cheese

GARNISH
3 tbsp chopped fresh parsley

1. Preheat oven to 400°F.
2. In a nonstick saucepan sprayed with cooking spray, heat 2 tsp of the oil over medium heat; cook onions and garlic for 5 minutes or until softened. Stir in peppers and sun-dried tomatoes; cook for 3 minutes. Stir in tomato sauce, chicken stock, basil, and oregano. Bring to a boil. Reduce heat to a simmer; cook, uncovered, for 10 minutes or until thickened.
3. Meanwhile, between 2 sheets of waxed paper, pound chicken breasts to an even 1/2-inch thickness. In a shallow bowl, whisk egg with water. On a separate plate, stir together bread crumbs and Parmesan cheese.
4. In a large nonstick skillet sprayed with cooking spray, heat remaining oil over medium-high heat. Dip each chicken breast in the egg mixture; coat each with the bread crumbs mixture. Cook for 5 minutes, turning once, or until golden on both sides.
5. Place half of sauce in a 9-inch casserole dish; place chicken on top. Spoon remaining sauce over top. Sprinkle with mozzarella and Parmesan. Bake, uncovered, for 10 minutes or until chicken is cooked through and cheese is melted. Sprinkle with parsley.

PREP: About 15 mins.
COOK: About 30 mins.

MAKES 4 SERVINGS

MAKE AHEAD
Cook sauce and bread chicken up to 1 day in advance. Bake just before serving. Freeze for up to 2 months.

NUTRITIONAL ANALYSIS PER SERVING
391 calories
38 g protein
11 g fat, total
2.9 g fat, saturated
35 g carbohydrates
440 mg sodium
127 mg cholesterol
4.8 g fibre

TIPS
For a change, try veal or pork scallops instead of the chicken. The sauce is delicious over pasta as well.

roasted chicken with plum tomatoes, green peppers, and olives

PREP: About 15 mins.
COOK: About 1-1/2 h.

MAKES 6 SERVINGS

MAKE AHEAD
Mix sauce up to 1 day in
advance. Freeze for up to
6 weeks

NUTRITIONAL ANALYSIS
PER SERVING
278 calories
35 g protein
7.7 g fat, total
2.2 g fat, saturated
17.1 g carbohydrates
538 mg sodium
103 mg cholesterol
4.2 g fibre

TIP
If you don't want to use a
whole chicken, you can use
2 legs and breasts with the
bone in and cook for half the
time.

I created this recipe—a nice diversion from plain old roasted chicken—for the Mövenpick restaurants in Toronto. It's so delicious, I knew I had to include it in this book. The vegetables and sauce form an outstanding natural gravy.

1 roasting chicken (about 3 lb)

SAUCE
3 cups diced plum tomatoes
1-1/2 cups diced onions
1-1/2 cups diced sweet green pepper
1/3 cup sliced black olives
2 tbsp minced garlic
1-1/2 tsp dried basil
1 tsp dried oregano
1-1/2 cups chicken stock
1 cup tomato pasta sauce
1/4 tsp salt and pepper

GARNISH
1/4 cup chopped fresh basil
1 oz light feta cheese, crumbled (optional)

1. Preheat oven to 425°F.
2. Spray roasting pan with cooking spray.
3. To make sauce: In a bowl, stir together sauce ingredients. Pour over chicken.
4. Bake uncovered for 45 minutes, basting occasionally. Reduce heat to 375°F; continue roasting for another 45 minutes or until chicken reaches an internal temperature of 165°F (check by inserting a meat thermometer) or chicken juices run clear.
5. Remove and discard skin before serving. Spoon vegetable mixture over chicken. Serve sprinkled with basil and feta (if using).

chicken with soy molasses sauce

Boneless chicken breasts will be moist if coated with cornstarch or flour before cooking. In light cooking, you can't use the same amount of oil or fat to cook with, so the coating helps to maintain the moisture in the chicken. The sauce produced is thick and rich tasting.

6 boneless skinless chicken breasts (about 1-1/2 lb total)
1/4 cup cornstarch
2 tsp vegetable oil

SAUCE
1/3 cup brown sugar
1/3 cup low-sodium soy sauce
1/4 cup water
2 tbsp molasses
1 tbsp cornstarch
1 tsp minced garlic
1 tsp chopped gingerroot

GARNISH
1/4 cup chopped fresh coriander
1/4 cup chopped green onions

1. Preheat oven to 425°F. Spray a 9-inch baking dish with cooking spray.
2. Dust chicken with cornstarch. In a nonstick skillet sprayed with cooking spray, heat oil over medium-high heat; cook chicken for 5 minutes, turning once, or until browned. Do not cook through. Transfer to prepared baking dish.
3. To make sauce: In a bowl, stir sauce ingredients together until smooth. Pour over chicken.
4. Bake uncovered in centre of oven for 15 to 20 minutes, turning halfway, or until chicken is just cooked through and sauce is slightly thickened.
5. Serve sprinkled with coriander and green onions.

PREP: About 5 mins.
COOK: About 15 mins.

MAKES 6 SERVINGS

MAKE AHEAD
Sauté chicken and prepare sauce up to 1 day in advance. Bake just before serving. Freeze for up to 6 weeks.

NUTRITIONAL ANALYSIS
PER SERVING
214 calories
27.2 g protein
3 g fat, total
0.5 g fat, saturated
19.6 g carbohydrates
580 mg sodium
65.8 mg cholesterol
0.3 g fibre

TIP
To hasten the molasses (or honey or maple or corn syrup) off the spoon, first spray the spoon with vegetable oil.

greek-style chicken

PREP: About 15 mins.
COOK: About 18 mins.

MAKES 4 SERVINGS

MAKE AHEAD
Cook sauce up to 1 day in advance. Just before serving, add chicken, and cook as in Step 2. Freeze for up to 6 weeks.

NUTRITIONAL ANALYSIS PER SERVING
245 calories
30 g protein
8.5 g fat, total
1.4 g fat, saturated
12 g carbohydrates
396 mg sodium
68 mg cholesterol
1.7 g fibre

TIPS
Feta and goat cheese are lower in fat and calories than other hard cheeses. The milk fat (MF) content is about 15% or less compared with 25% or more in regular cheeses.

This is one of the best simmered chicken dishes I've ever created. Often, the chicken in such dishes can be tough or flavorless, but the Greek-style ingredients in this recipe tenderize the chicken, leaving it succulent and tender.

4 boneless skinless chicken breasts (about 1 lb total)
3 tbsp all-purpose flour
1 tbsp vegetable oil
1 cup chopped onions
1 tsp minced garlic
1 cup diced plum tomatoes
2/3 cup chicken stock
1/3 cup sliced black olives
1-1/2 tsp dried oregano
1 oz light feta cheese, crumbled

GARNISH
1/4 cup chopped fresh parsley, as garnish

1. Between 2 sheets of waxed paper, pound chicken breasts to an even 1/2-inch thickness. Dust with flour. In a large nonstick skillet sprayed with cooking spray, heat 2 tsp of the oil over medium-high heat; cook chicken for 5 minutes, turning once, or until golden on both sides. Do not cook through. Remove to clean plate.

2. In the same skillet, heat remaining oil over medium-high heat; cook onions and garlic for 2 minutes or until softened. Stir in plum tomatoes, chicken stock, olives, and oregano. Bring to a boil. Return chicken to pan. Reduce heat to medium-low. Cover, and cook for 8 minutes or until chicken is cooked through and sauce thickened. Sprinkle with feta cheese, cover, and cook 2 minutes longer or until feta melts. Serve garnished with parsley.

hoisin chicken with couscous

quick

PREP: About 10 mins.
COOK: About 15 mins.

MAKES 6 SERVINGS

MAKE AHEAD
Prepare the casserole 1 day in
advance. Reheat at 300°F
until warm. Freeze portions
for up to 3 months.

NUTRITIONAL ANALYSIS
PER SERVING
301 calories
31.4 g protein
2.4 g fat, total
0.5 g fat, saturated
38.4 g carbohydrates
495 mg sodium
66.1 mg cholesterol
2.1 g fibre

TIPS
Try boneless chicken thighs
for a real treat. Just remember to cook them longer. The
key to perfect couscous is to
spray your stock with some
cooking spray and keep the
couscous covered no longer
than 5 minutes.

This is a chicken dish that I teach at my "Weekday Wonders" class. It's always a hit because chicken is an international favorite. This hoisin orange sauce tastes wonderful, especially with the fluffy bed of couscous.

6 boneless skinless chicken breasts (about 1-1/2 lb total)

SAUCE
1/4 cup hoisin sauce
2 tbsp ketchup
2 tbsp orange juice concentrate, thawed
2 tbsp liquid honey
1 tbsp low-sodium soy sauce
1-1/2 tsp cornstarch
1 tsp minced garlic
1 tsp minced gingerroot
1/4 to 1/2 tsp hot Asian chili sauce

TOPPING
1 tsp toasted sesame seeds

COUSCOUS
1 cup chicken stock
1 cup couscous (cook couscous in last 5 minutes of oven time)

GARNISH
3 tbsp chopped fresh coriander or parsley

1. Preheat oven to 400°F. Spray a 9- × 12-inch casserole dish with cooking spray. Place chicken in prepared dish.

2. To make sauce: Mix sauce ingredients together until smooth; pour over chicken. Sprinkle with sesame seeds. Cover and bake in centre of oven for 15 minutes or until cooked through.

3. To make couscous: Meanwhile, bring stock to a boil. Add couscous. Cover, turn off heat, and let sit for 5 minutes. Uncover and fluff with a fork. Serve chicken over couscous. Garnish with coriander.

PREP: About 10 mins.
COOK: About 15 mins.

MAKES 4 SERVINGS

MAKE AHEAD
Sauté chicken and prepare
sauce up to 1 day in advance.
Bake just before serving.
Freeze for up to 6 weeks.

NUTRITIONAL ANALYSIS
PER SERVING
264 calories
27.8 g protein
4.7 g fat, total
0.7 g fat, saturated
27.7 g carbohydrates
337 mg sodium
66.3 mg cholesterol
1.1 g fibre

TIPS
Make sure always to buy pure
maple syrup (the flavored
ones are mostly corn syrup).
To toast your own sesame
seeds, sauté in a skillet on
high heat for 2 minutes or
until just lightly browned.

chicken with maple syrup hoisin glaze

The combination of maple syrup and hoisin is wonderful. This is a meal my family loves to eat a couple of times a week. I often serve it over couscous or rice.

4 boneless skinless chicken breasts (about 1 lb total)
3 tbsp all-purpose flour
2 tsp vegetable oil

SAUCE
1/4 cup maple syrup
1/4 cup hoisin sauce
3 tbsp orange juice
2 tsp minced garlic

TOPPING
1 tsp toasted sesame seeds

GARNISH
1/4 cup chopped fresh parsley or coriander

1. Preheat oven to 400°F. Spray a 9-inch baking dish with cooking spray.
2. Dust chicken with flour. In a nonstick skillet sprayed with cooking spray, heat oil over medium-high heat. Cook chicken for 5 minutes, turning once, or until browned. Do not cook through.
3. To make sauce: In a small bowl, stir together sauce ingredients. Pour over chicken. Sprinkle with sesame seeds.
4. Bake, uncovered, in centre of oven for 10 to 15 minutes or until chicken is cooked through. Serve sprinkled with parsley.

chicken breasts with pineapple hoisin sauce

This wonderful chicken dish is fresh tasting, simple, and quick to prepare. Dusting the chicken with flour retains the juices without using excess oil.

6 boneless skinless chicken breasts (about 1-1/2 lb total)
1/4 cup all-purpose flour
2 tsp vegetable oil

SAUCE
1/3 cup diced pineapple (fresh or canned)
5 tbsp hoisin sauce
1/4 cup dried cranberries
1/4 cup pineapple juice
2 tbsp low-sodium soy sauce
1 tbsp liquid honey
1 tbsp rice vinegar
1 tsp minced garlic
1/2 tsp hot sauce

GARNISH
1/4 cup chopped fresh basil or coriander

1. Preheat oven to 425°F. Spray a 9-inch baking dish with cooking spray.
2. Dust chicken with flour. In a nonstick skillet sprayed with cooking spray, heat oil over medium-high heat. Cook chicken breasts for 5 minutes, turning once, or until browned on both sides. Do not cook through. Transfer to prepared baking dish.
3. To make sauce: In a bowl, stir together sauce ingredients. Pour over chicken. Bake, uncovered, for 10 to 15 minutes or until chicken is cooked through. Serve sprinkled with basil.

PREP: About 10 mins.
COOK: About 15 mins.

MAKES 6 SERVINGS

MAKE AHEAD
Cook chicken and prepare sauce up to 1 day in advance. Freeze together for up to 2 months. Bake chicken and sauce together just before serving.

NUTRITIONAL ANALYSIS PER SERVING
222 calories
27.7 g protein
3.6 g fat, total
0.6 g fat, saturated
19.8 g carbohydrates
450 mg sodium
66.2 mg cholesterol
1.2 g fibre

TIPS
Fresh pineapple is best, but if necessary use canned chunks along with the juice from the can. I keep frozen pineapple juice concentrate on hand and mix about 1 tbsp frozen juice with 1/4 cup water for the juice needed in this recipe.

chicken breasts with maple syrup applesauce glaze

I had a great chicken meal in a restaurant, so I asked the chef the secret ingredient in the sauce. When he told me it was applesauce, I was shocked. I've tried to duplicate that recipe. The combination of applesauce, maple syrup, and ketchup goes great with chicken.

6 boneless skinless chicken breasts (about 1-1/2 lb total)
3 tbsp all-purpose flour
1 tsp vegetable oil

GLAZE
1 cup diced onions
1/2 cup unsweetened applesauce
1/2 cup maple syrup
1/3 cup ketchup
2 tbsp cider vinegar
2 tsp minced garlic
1/2 tsp hot sauce

GARNISH
1/4 cup chopped fresh parsley

1. Preheat oven to 425°F. Spray a 9-inch baking dish with cooking spray.
2. Dust chicken with flour. In a nonstick skillet sprayed with cooking spray, heat oil over medium-high heat. Cook chicken breasts for 5 minutes, turning once, or until browned. Do not cook through. Transfer to prepared baking dish.
3. To make glaze: Respray pan. Cook onions over medium heat for 5 minutes or until browned. Stir in remaining ingredients. Pour over chicken.
4. Bake uncovered in centre of oven for 10 to 15 minutes or just until chicken is cooked through, turning over halfway through cooking.
5. Serve garnished with parsley.

PREP: About 10 mins.
COOK: About 20 mins.

MAKES 6 SERVINGS

MAKE AHEAD
Sauté chicken and prepare glaze up to 1 day in advance. Bake just before serving. Freeze for up to 6 weeks.

NUTRITIONAL ANALYSIS PER SERVING
260 calories
27.3 g protein
3.2 g fat, total
1.5 g fat, saturated
30.4 g carbohydrates
250 mg sodium
65.8 mg cholesterol
1.2 g fibre

TIPS
Be sure to buy unsweetened applesauce—and do buy the smaller bottles since the larger ones spoil quickly. If you do have too much applesauce, just freeze in small containers.

chicken with coconut pineapple sauce

I don't use pineapple juice often in my recipes, but it has such a wonderful flavor that I should remember to do so.

6 boneless skinless chicken breasts (about 1-1/2 lb total)
3 tbsp all-purpose flour
2 tsp vegetable oil

SAUCE
1/3 cup light coconut milk
3 tbsp pineapple or orange juice
2 tbsp low-sodium soy sauce
1 tbsp fresh lemon juice
1 tbsp brown sugar
1-1/2 tsp cornstarch
1 tsp minced garlic
1 tsp minced gingerroot
1/2 tsp hot sauce

GARNISH
1/4 cup chopped fresh coriander or parsley

1. Preheat oven to 425°F. Spray a 9-inch baking dish with cooking spray.
2. Dust chicken with flour. In a nonstick skillet sprayed with cooking spray, heat oil over medium-high heat. Cook chicken breasts for 5 minutes, turning once, or until browned. Do not cook through. Transfer to prepared baking dish.
3. To make sauce: In a bowl, stir together sauce ingredients until cornstarch is dissolved. Pour over chicken.
4. Bake uncovered in centre of oven for 15 minutes or just until chicken is cooked through, turning over halfway. Serve garnished with coriander.

PREP: About 10 mins.
COOK: About 20 mins.

MAKES 6 SERVINGS

MAKE AHEAD
Sauté chicken and prepare sauce up to 1 day in advance. Freeze together for up to 2 months. Bake just before serving.

NUTRITIONAL ANALYSIS PER SERVING
170 calories
27.1 g protein
3.7 g fat, total
1.1 g fat, saturated
7.1 g carbohydrates
289 mg sodium
65.8 mg cholesterol
0.2 g fibre

TIPS
I always keep a container of frozen pineapple juice concentrate on hand. For the 3 tbsp juice needed in this recipe, mix 2 tsp frozen juice concentrate with 3 tbsp water.

PREP: About 10 mins.
COOK: About 10 mins.

MAKES 6 SERVINGS

MAKE AHEAD
Prepare sauce up to 3 days
in advance. Freeze for up to
6 weeks.

NUTRITIONAL ANALYSIS
PER SERVING
238.5 calories
26.9 g protein
4.5 g fat, total
0.7 g fat, saturated
22.6 g carbohydrates
284 mg sodium
66 mg cholesterol
0.3 g fibre

TIPS
If you find marmalade too
tart, substitute apricot jam.
Always keep a container of
orange juice concentrate in
the freezer for cooking and
baking purposes.

chicken with honey and orange marmalade glaze

Marmalade is not only great on toast, but also wonderful as part of a sauce for chicken or fish. A jar will last forever in your refrigerator! Always have one on hand.

6 boneless skinless chicken breasts (about 1-1/2 lb total)
3 tbsp cornstarch
2 tsp vegetable oil

SAUCE
3 tbsp orange marmalade
3 tbsp liquid honey
2 tbsp orange juice concentrate, thawed
2 tbsp low-sodium soy sauce
2 tsp sesame oil
1 tsp minced garlic
1 tsp cornstarch
1/2 tsp minced gingerroot

GARNISH
1/4 cup chopped fresh parsley

1. Between 2 sheets of waxed paper, pound chicken breasts to an even 1/2-inch thickness. Dust chicken with cornstarch. In a nonstick skillet sprayed with cooking spray, heat oil over medium-high heat. Cook chicken for 5 to 8 minutes, turning once, or until cooked through. Place on a serving dish.
2. To make sauce: In a small saucepan, stir together sauce ingredients until cornstarch is dissolved. Cook over medium heat for 4 minutes or until slightly thickened.
3. Pour sauce over chicken. Serve garnished with parsley.

turkey scaloppini with roasted peppers, cheese, and rose's light pesto

Turkey is a wonderful substitute for chicken and actually is leaner and lower in fat. Most super-markets today sell boneless turkey breasts, as well as turkey scaloppini. If you can find only turkey breasts, either pound them until thin or slice horizontally in half.

1 egg
2 tbsp water or low-fat milk
2/3 cup dry seasoned bread crumbs
1-1/2 lb turkey scaloppini
2 tsp vegetable oil
1/4 cup Rose's Light Pesto (recipe on next page) or store-bought
3 oz roasted sweet red peppers, thinly sliced (either bottled in water or roasted at home)
1/3 cup grated light mozzarella cheese

1. Preheat oven to 425°F. Spray a 9-inch baking dish with cooking spray.
2. In a shallow bowl, whisk egg with water. Place bread crumbs on a plate. Dip turkey in egg mixture and then in bread crumbs.
3. In a nonstick skillet sprayed with cooking spray, heat oil over medium-high heat. Cook turkey for 3 minutes, turning once, or until browned. Do not cook through. Transfer to prepared baking dish. Spread with pesto. Sprinkle with roasted peppers and mozzarella cheese.
4. Bake uncovered in centre of oven for 5 minutes until cheese is melted and turkey is cooked through.

super
quick

PREP: About 5 mins.
COOK: About 8 mins.

MAKES 6 SERVINGS

MAKE AHEAD
Bread scaloppini up to 1 day in advance. Bake just before serving. Freeze for up to 6 weeks.

NUTRITIONAL ANALYSIS
PER SERVING
213 calories
34.6 g protein
7.8 g fat, total
2.6 g fat, saturated
11.1 g carbohydrates
425 mg sodium
113 mg cholesterol
1 g fibre

TIPS
Be sure to buy roasted peppers packed in water, not in oil. To roast your own, preheat the oven to 450°F and roast peppers for 20 to 25 minutes or until charred on all sides. If you're in a hurry to peel them, first run them under cold water.

rose's light pesto

Making your own pesto rather than using store-bought saves you about half the calories and fat.

1 cup packed fresh basil leaves

2 tbsp grated Parmesan cheese

1 tbsp toasted pine nuts

1 oz light cream cheese

1 tsp crushed garlic

3 tbsp chicken stock, vegetable stock, or water

2 tbsp olive oil

In a food processor, purée the ingredients until smooth. If too thick, add another tablespoon of stock.

PREP: About 5 mins.

MAKES 1/2 CUP

MAKE AHEAD
You can refrigerate pesto for up to 1 week or freeze for up to 3 months.

NUTRITIONAL ANALYSIS
PER TABLESPOON
48 calories
1 g protein
2.8 g fat, total
0.4 g fat, saturated
0.3 g carbohydrates
39 mg sodium
2.9 mg cholesterol
1.9 g fibre

TIP
Use the amount of pesto indicated in the recipes in this book. Use over pasta, fish, or chicken.

fish and seafood

grilled halibut with yellow pepper sauce

PREP: About 10 mins.
COOK: About 20 mins.

MAKES 6 SERVINGS

MAKE AHEAD
Sauce can be made up to
3 days in advance. Freeze for
up to 3 months. Freeze
cooked fish for up to 2 weeks.

NUTRITIONAL ANALYSIS
PER SERVING
203 calories
24 g protein
9.2 g fat, total
1.6 g fat, saturated
6 g carbohydrates
161 mg sodium
65 mg cholesterol
0.9 g fibre

TIPS
Before eating fish, always
remove the skin. It contains
excess fat that is not the
heart-healthy type.
Evaporated milk has the consistency of cream without the
calories and fat.

This curry-flavored sweet yellow pepper sauce goes beautifully with almost any variety of fish. Yellow peppers contain a powerful antioxidant effective in the fight against cancer. Feel free to vary the recipe by grilling the peppers or substituting sweet red peppers.

SAUCE
2 tsp olive oil
1 medium sweet yellow pepper, chopped
1/2 cup chopped onions
1 tsp minced garlic
1/4 tsp salt
1/8 tsp freshly ground black pepper
1/4 tsp curry powder
3 tbsp 2% evaporated milk

6 skin-on halibut fillets (about 4 oz each)

GARNISH
3 tbsp chopped fresh coriander or parsley

1. To make sauce: In a nonstick skillet, heat olive oil over medium heat. Add peppers, onions, garlic, salt, pepper, and curry; cook for 10 minutes or until vegetables are soft. Transfer mixture to a blender. Add evaporated milk; purée until smooth. Return to pan, keeping warm.
2. Either on a barbecue or in a grill pan sprayed with cooking spray, cook fish over medium-high heat for 10 minutes per inch thickness of fish, or until fish flakes easily when prodded with a fork. (Alternatively, cook in a preheated 425°F oven for 10 minutes per inch thickness.)
3. Remove fish skin. Spoon sauce over fish; sprinkle with coriander.

cornmeal-crusted sea bass with tomato salsa

If you're tired of bread coating on fish, try adding some cornmeal. It gives a beautiful yellow crust that has a delicious crunchy texture and goes well with any fish, especially sea bass. The tomato salsa suits the fish perfectly.

1 egg

2 tbsp water

1/4 cup dry seasoned bread crumbs

3 tbsp cornmeal

2 tbsp chopped fresh parsley or basil

1/4 tsp freshly ground black pepper

2 tsp vegetable oil

1 lb skinless sea bass fillet or other firm white fish

SALSA

1-1/2 cups finely diced tomatoes

1/4 cup finely diced sweet onions

2 tbsp finely chopped fresh parsley or basil

1 tbsp fresh lemon juice

2 tsp olive oil

1 tsp granulated sugar

1/2 tsp minced garlic

1/2 tsp hot chili sauce or minced jalapeño pepper

1. Preheat oven to 425°F.
2. In a shallow bowl, beat egg with water. On a plate, stir together bread crumbs, cornmeal, parsley, and pepper.
3. In a large nonstick skillet sprayed with cooking spray, heat oil over medium-high heat. Dip fish in egg mixture; coat fish with cornmeal mixture. Cook for 2 minutes, turning once, or until golden on both sides. Transfer to a rimmed baking sheet. Bake in centre of oven for 8 minutes or until fish flakes easily when prodded with a fork.
4. To make salsa: Meanwhile, in a bowl, stir salsa ingredients together. Serve fish with salsa on the side.

 quick

PREP: About 15 mins.
COOK: About 10 mins.

MAKES 4 SERVINGS

MAKE AHEAD
Coat fish and prepare sauce (with seeded tomatoes) up to 1 day in advance. Freeze cooked fish, but not the salsa, for up to 2 weeks.

NUTRITIONAL ANALYSIS PER SERVING
242 calories
25 g protein
8.7 g fat, total
1.5 g fat, saturated
16 g carbohydrates
300 mg sodium
100 mg cholesterol
1.9 g fibre

TIPS
Do not cook the fish until just ready to serve. If you choose to use regular field tomatoes, it's best to seed them to avoid excess water. If yellow tomatoes are in season, combine them with other kinds of tomatoes.

pecan-coated sea bass with pineapple sauce

PREP: About 15 mins.
COOK: About 12 mins.

MAKES 6 SERVINGS

MAKE AHEAD
Fish can be breaded up to
1 day in advance. Cooked fish
can be frozen for up to
2 weeks.

NUTRITIONAL ANALYSIS
PER SERVING
167 calories
23.7 g protein
11.8 g fat, total
1.7 g fat, saturated
14 g carbohydrates
142 mg sodium
82 mg cholesterol
1 g fibre

TIPS
Substitute any other firm flavorful fish for the sea bass.
Salmon or halibut are good
choices.

The flavors of pecans, a distinct-tasting white fish, and a pineapple sauce make this an outstanding recipe. If you don't regularly have pineapple juice at home, buy some frozen juice concentrate to keep on hand.

1/4 cup pecan halves
1/3 cup dry unseasoned bread crumbs
1 egg
2 tbsp low-fat milk or water
2 tsp vegetable oil
6 skinless sea bass fillets (about 4 oz each)

SAUCE
1/3 cup pineapple or orange juice
2 tbsp liquid honey
1 tsp finely grated lemon rind

GARNISH
1/4 cup finely chopped green onions
3 tbsp chopped fresh parsley

1. Preheat oven to 425°F. Spray baking sheet with cooking spray.
2. In a food processor, coarsely chop pecans with bread crumbs by turning processor on and off. Place pecan mixture on a plate. In a shallow bowl, combine egg and milk.
3. In a nonstick skillet sprayed with cooking spray, heat oil over medium-high heat. Dip fish into egg mixture; coat fish with pecan mixture. Cook fish just until browned on all sides, about 5 minutes. Do not cook through. Transfer to prepared baking sheet. Bake in centre of oven just until fish flakes easily when prodded with a fork, about another 5 minutes. Place on a serving dish.
4. To make sauce: Stir sauce ingredients together in a small saucepan. Cook over medium heat for 2 minutes until slightly thickened. Pour sauce over sea bass. Sprinkle with green onions and parsley.

tilapia with coconut peanut sauce

Tilapia is a popular white fish to serve these days. It has a mild flavor and a good texture, and goes beautifully with any stronger-flavored sauce.

1-1/2 lb tilapia fillet or other thin firm white fish (whole or cut into 6 fillets)

SAUCE
1/4 cup light coconut milk
1 tbsp natural peanut butter
1 tsp low-sodium soy sauce
1 tsp rice wine vinegar
1 tsp liquid honey
1/2 tsp finely chopped garlic
1/2 tsp finely chopped gingerroot

GARNISH
1/4 cup chopped fresh coriander or parsley
1 tbsp finely chopped unsalted dry roasted peanuts

1. Either on a barbecue or in a nonstick grill pan sprayed with cooking spray, cook tilapia over medium-high heat for 3 minutes per side or just until cooked. Place on a serving dish.
2. To make sauce: Combine sauce ingredients in a small saucepan. Cook over medium heat for 1 minute or just until warm and mixed. Pour sauce over fish. Sprinkle with coriander and peanuts.

super
quick

PREP: About 5 mins.
COOK: About 8 mins.

MAKES 6 SERVINGS

MAKE AHEAD
Sauce can be prepared up to 3 days in advance and frozen for up to 2 months. Cooked fish can be frozen for up to 2 weeks.

NUTRITIONAL ANALYSIS PER SERVING
130 calories
21 g protein
3.3 g fat, total
0.9 g fat, saturated
2.2 g carbohydrates
96 mg sodium
5.1 mg cholesterol
0.3 g fibre

TIPS
Light coconut milk is available in most supermarkets. It contains 75 percent less fat and calories than regular coconut milk, which is highly saturated.

super quick

PREP: About 10 mins.
COOK: About 10 mins.

MAKES 6 SERVINGS

MAKE AHEAD
Sauce can be prepared up to
3 days in advance and frozen
for up to 1 month. Freeze
cooked fish up to 2 weeks.

NUTRITIONAL ANALYSIS
PER SERVING
120 calories
18 g protein
3.8 g fat, total
0.7 g fat, saturated
6.1 g carbohydrates
124 mg sodium
28 mg cholesterol
0.6 g fibre

TIPS
Substitute any white fish of
your choice. You can use the
sauce over cooked vegeta-
bles, pasta, or chicken.

asian-flavored halibut

The flavors of spinach, basil, orange, and the Asian ingredients mingle in this dish and are an unusual and delicious combination. Baby spinach has a milder and more delicate texture than regular spinach.

6 skin-on halibut fillets (about 4 oz each)

SAUCE
1 cup well-packed baby spinach leaves
1/2 cup well-packed chopped fresh basil
1/4 cup chopped green onions
2 tbsp orange juice concentrate, thawed
1 tbsp hoisin sauce
1 tbsp oyster sauce
1 tbsp water
2 tsp packed brown sugar
2 tsp sesame oil
2 tsp rice wine vinegar
1 tsp minced garlic
1 tsp minced gingerroot

1. Preheat barbecue. On grill sprayed with cooking spray, cook halibut over medium-high heat for 10 minutes per inch thickness of fish, turning once, or until fish flakes easily when prodded with a fork. (Alternatively, bake in centre of a preheated 425°F oven for 10 minutes per inch or until fish flakes easily when prodded with a fork.)
2. To make sauce: Meanwhile, in a food processor, purée sauce ingredients together until smooth.
3. Remove fish skin. Spoon sauce over fish.

potato-crusted white fish with tartar sauce

The inspiration for this recipe is the traditional potato pancake (latke). I thought that finely chopped potatoes would taste great if they formed a crust on fish. They definitely do! The tartar sauce is a tasty accompaniment.

1 large potato, peeled and finely cut into chunks (about 3/4 lb)
3 tbsp minced green onions
2 tbsp chopped fresh dill
1-1/2 tsp minced garlic
1/4 tsp salt
1/8 tsp freshly ground black pepper
2 tsp vegetable oil
1 lb skinless firm white fish fillet, such as halibut, cod, or sea bass, about 1-inch thick

SAUCE
1/3 cup light sour cream
1 tbsp light mayonnaise
1 tbsp chopped fresh dill
2 tsp fresh lemon juice
1/2 tsp Dijon mustard

1. Preheat oven to 425°F.
2. In a food processor, finely chop potatoes. Squeeze out excess moisture. In a bowl, stir together potatoes, green onions, dill, garlic, and salt and pepper. In a nonstick skillet sprayed with cooking spray, heat oil over medium heat. Firmly press half of potato mixture onto one side of fish Carefully place fish potato side down in skillet. Press fish firmly with a spatula and cook for 5 minutes on medium-high heat or until potato is browned. During the cooking, press the remaining potato on top of the fish. With a spatula, carefully turn fish over. Cook for another 5 minutes until fish is just cooked or until potato is browned. If fish is thicker than 1 inch, finish cooking in a preheated oven at 425°F for 5 minutes or until done.
3. To make sauce: In a bowl, stir sauce ingredients together. Serve fish with sauce.

PREP: About 15 mins.
COOK: About 12 mins.

MAKES 4 SERVINGS

MAKE AHEAD
Sauce can be made up to 2 days in advance. Freeze cooked fish for up to 2 weeks.

NUTRITIONAL ANALYSIS PER SERVING
200 calories
23 g protein
7.6 g fat, total
1.7 g fat, saturated
10 g carbohydrates
204 mg sodium
44 mg cholesterol
0.6 g fibre

TIPS
Don't peel potatoes until ready to use or they will turn brown. Alternatively, place them in cold water until ready to use.

whole fish stuffed with couscous, lemon, feta cheese, and oregano

A whole stuffed fish is outstanding to serve for a larger group. Most people don't like serving a whole fish because they don't know how to deal with the bones. I ask the fish counter staff at my supermarket to butterfly the fish, removing the entire backbone so that the fish can easily be stuffed and served without bones. This stuffing is delicious on its own as well.

3 lb butterflied whole fish, such as arctic char, whitefish, or red snapper
1 to 2 tsp crushed garlic
1/3 cup fish stock or white wine

STUFFING
1 cup chicken or vegetable stock	3/4 tsp minced garlic
1 cup couscous	3/4 oz light feta cheese, crumbled
1/4 cup chopped green onions	2 tbsp chopped fresh parsley
3 tbsp chopped sweet red peppers	2 tbsp fresh lemon juice
2 tbsp olive oil	1/2 tsp dried oregano

1. Preheat oven to 425°F. Line a baking sheet with foil and spray with cooking spray.
2. Place fish on prepared baking sheet. Rub with crushed garlic and spray with cooking spray. Pour fish stock into baking sheet.
3. To make stuffing: Bring stock to a boil. Add couscous. Cover, remove from heat, and let stand for 5 minutes. Fluff with a fork and cool slightly. Add remaining stuffing ingredients to couscous; mix well.
4. Stuff fish with one-quarter of couscous mixture, being careful not to overstuff. Place remaining stuffing in a covered casserole dish.
5. Bake fish in centre of oven for 20 to 25 minutes or until temperature on a meat thermometer reaches 145°F. (If you don't have a meat thermometer, bake for 10 minutes per inch including the stuffing.) Heat remaining stuffing in oven during the last 5 minutes of cooking time. Serve fish with extra stuffing on the side.

PREP: About 10 mins.
COOK: About 25 to 30 mins.

MAKES 8 SERVINGS

MAKE AHEAD
Prepare stuffing up to 1 day in advance. Don't stuff fish until ready to bake. Cook fish early in day only if you will serve at room temperature. Freeze cooked fish and stuffing for up to 2 weeks.

NUTRITIONAL ANALYSIS PER SERVING
390 calories
35 g protein
12 g fat, total
3.1 g fat, saturated
18 g carbohydrates
118 mg sodium
124 mg cholesterol
1.4 g fibre

TIPS
The secret to producing perfect fluffy couscous is to spray a small amount of vegetable oil into the cooking liquid and cover the pot for only 5 minutes.

grilled tuna with greek tomato salsa

This Mediterranean-flavored dish tastes like a Greek salad. Tuna goes well with the salsa. Sea bass would too.

SALSA
1 cup diced plum tomatoes
1/3 cup diced sweet green peppers
1/4 cup diced green onions
3 tbsp chopped black olives
2 tbsp fresh lemon juice
1-1/2 oz light feta cheese, crumbled
2 tsp olive oil
1-1/2 tsp finely chopped garlic
1/2 tsp dried oregano

6 tuna fillets (about 4 oz each)

GARNISH
1/4 cup chopped fresh basil or parsley

1. To make salsa: In a bowl, stir salsa ingredients together.
2. Either on a barbecue or in a nonstick grill pan sprayed with cooking spray, cook tuna for 4 minutes per side or just until fish is cooked through. Place on a serving dish. Sprinkle with basil. Serve salsa on the side.

PREP: About 15 mins.
COOK: About 8 to 10 mins.

MAKES 6 SERVINGS

MAKE AHEAD
Salsa can be made up to 1 day in advance (use seeded tomatoes). Cooked fish can be frozen for up to 2 weeks.

NUTRITIONAL ANALYSIS PER SERVING
183 calories
24.3 g protein
7.2 g fat, total
1.9 g fat, saturated
4.2 g carbohydrates
237 mg sodium
47 mg cholesterol
1 g fibre

TIP
If you want some heat, add 1 tsp minced jalepeño peppers.

PREP: About 10 mins.
COOK: About 10 mins.

MAKES 6 SERVINGS

MAKE AHEAD
The filling can be prepared up
to 3 days in advance. Freeze
cooked fish for up to 2 weeks.

NUTRITIONAL ANALYSIS
PER SERVING
150 calories
23 g protein
5.3 g fat, total
1.6 g fat, saturated
11 g carbohydrates
161 mg sodium
61 mg cholesterol
0 g fibre

TIPS
You can either make a slit all
the way down the length of
the salmon or make a shorter,
deeper slit into which to stuff
the cheese mixture. Be sure
not to overcook the fish.

salmon with ricotta dill filling

I was served a dish similar to this in a beautiful resort in the Muskoka region of Ontario. That dish had a cream sauce poured over top. I asked the chef what the basic ingredients were in the stuffing and created my own light version. It's delicious, unusual, and doesn't need any extra sauce. Salmon is one of the healthiest fish for you because it contains omega-3 fatty acids, which can help to lower the bad kind of cholesterol, reduce the risk of heart disease, and help in preventing cancer.

FILLING
1/4 cup smooth light ricotta cheese
1 oz light feta cheese, crumbled
1/2 oz light cream cheese, softened
1 tbsp fresh lemon juice
1/2 tsp minced garlic
1/4 tsp Dijon mustard
2 tbsp fresh chopped dill

6 skin-on salmon fillets (about 4 oz each)

GARNISH
2 tbsp chopped fresh dill or chives, as garnish

1. Preheat oven to 425°F. Spray a baking sheet with cooking spray.
2. To make filling: In a food processor or in a bowl using an electric mixer, purée all filling ingredients, except dill, until smooth. Stir in dill.
3. Place salmon skin side down on baking sheet. Make a slit down the centre of each salmon fillet to within 1/2 inch of either end, being careful not to cut right through the flesh. Fill the slit with cheese mixture.
4. Bake in centre of oven for 10 minutes per inch thickness of fish or just until barely done in centre. Remove fish skin. Garnish with dill.

salmon stuffed with cheese and wrapped in phyllo

super
quick

PREP: About 10 mins.
COOK: About 10 mins.

MAKES 8 SERVINGS

MAKE AHEAD
The filling can be prepared up
to 3 days in advance and
refrigerated. Phyllo-wrapped
fish, uncooked, can be frozen
for up to 2 weeks and baked
frozen.

NUTRITIONAL ANALYSIS
PER SERVING
260 calories
22 g protein
12 g fat, total
3.4 g fat, saturated
9 g carbohydrates
200 mg sodium
70 mg cholesterol
0.4 g fibre

Phyllo intimidates many cooks, but it's really quite easy to work with. Two rules: work quickly and keep the phyllo you are not working with covered. By spraying the phyllo with cooking spray, you avoid the excess fat of the butter traditionally used to prepare the thin phyllo pastry sheets.

FILLING
1/3 cup smooth light ricotta cheese
1 oz light cream cheese, softened
2 tsp fresh lemon juice
2 tsp light mayonnaise
1/2 tsp minced garlic
1 tbsp chopped fresh dill
1 oz chopped smoked salmon

4 skinless salmon fillets (about 8 oz each)
6 sheets phyllo pastry

1. Preheat oven to 400°F. Spray rimmed baking sheet with cooking spray.
2. To make filling: In a food processor or in a bowl, mix cheeses, juice, mayonnaise, and garlic until smooth. Stir in dill and smoked salmon. Make a slit down the centre of each salmon fillet to within 1/2 inch of either end, being careful not to cut right through the flesh. Fill the slit with cheese mixture.
3. On work surface, place 3 sheets of phyllo one on top of the other, spraying between sheets with cooking spray. Cut in half lengthwise. Place a stuffed salmon fillet, slit side down, in the middle of each strip of phyllo. Wrap phyllo over salmon to fully enclose. Place seam side down on prepared baking sheet. Repeat with remaining phyllo and salmon. Spray bundles with cooking spray.
4. Bake in centre of oven for 10 to 15 minutes or just until internal temperature of fish reaches 140°F on a meat thermometer or until a knife inserted in the centre of the fish comes out warm. Cut phyllo packets in half diagonally before serving.

salmon with black bean mango salsa

PREP: About 10 mins.
COOK: About 20 mins.

MAKES 6 SERVINGS

MAKE AHEAD
Salsa can be made up to
2 days in advance. Cooked
salmon can be frozen for
up to 2 weeks.

NUTRITIONAL ANALYSIS
PER SERVING
206 calories
24.1 g protein
7.5 g fat, total
1.2 g fat, saturated
10.4 g carbohydrates
178 mg sodium
62 mg cholesterol
7.5 g fibre

TIP
The sweetest mangoes and
those that most consistently
taste good are the Indonesian
variety; these are small and
golden yellow.

The combination of black beans and sweet mango is outstanding. I serve this salsa over chicken, other fish, and even as a salad dressing. Sautéing the corn adds a barbecued flavor.

SALSA
1/2 cup drained canned corn
1/2 cup diced mango
1/2 cup rinsed and drained canned black beans
1/4 cup diced sweet red peppers
1/4 cup diced sweet onions
1/4 cup chopped fresh coriander or parsley
1 tbsp fresh lime or lemon juice
1 tsp liquid honey
1 tsp minced garlic
1/2 tsp hot pepper sauce

6 skin-on salmon fillets (about 4 oz each)

1. To make salsa: In a nonstick skillet sprayed with cooking spray, cook corn on medium-high heat for 8 minutes or just until corn is dry and beginning to brown. Place in a serving dish. Stir in remaining salsa ingredients.
2. Either on a barbecue or in a nonstick grill pan sprayed with cooking spray, grill salmon on medium-high heat for 5 minutes per side or just until medium done (10 minutes per inch of fish thickness). Serve salsa over top of fish.

salmon with maple hoisin sauce

The combination of maple syrup and hoisin sauce is wonderful. The Dijon mustard cuts the sweetness and adds a great flavor to the salmon.

SAUCE

1/4 cup maple syrup

2 tbsp hoisin sauce

1 tbsp balsamic vinegar

2 tsp Dijon mustard

1/2 tsp minced garlic

1/4 tsp minced gingerroot

4 skin-on salmon fillets (about 4 oz each)

GARNISH

2 tbsp chopped fresh parsley

1. Preheat oven to 425°F. Spray a rimmed baking sheet with cooking spray.
2. To make sauce: In a bowl, stir sauce ingredients together.
3. Place salmon skin side down on prepared baking sheet. Brush half the maple syrup mixture over fish. Bake in centre of oven for 10 minutes per inch thickness of fish or until fish flakes easily when prodded with a fork. Remove fish skin before serving. Garnish with parsley and serve with remaining sauce.

PREP: About 5 mins.
COOK: About 10 mins.

MAKES 4 SERVINGS

MAKE AHEAD
Prepare sauce up to 1 week in advance. Freeze cooked fish for up to 2 weeks.

NUTRITIONAL ANALYSIS
PER SERVING
235 calories
23 g protein
7.9 g fat, total
1.2 g fat, saturated
18 g carbohydrates
245 mg sodium
64 mg cholesterol
0.3 g fibre

TIPS
You can also grill the fish on a barbecue or in a grill pan sprayed with cooking spray, and simmer the sauce until thick before serving over the fish. If you grate excess ginger or garlic, freeze it in ice cube trays or in small baggies to use later as needed.

sesame-crusted salmon with asian sauce

This is a wonderful recipe to serve as a dinner or as part of a buffet served at room temperature. The oyster mushrooms have a firm texture and give the sauce a great flavor.

SAUCE
2 tsp vegetable oil
1/2 cup chopped onions
1 cup chopped oyster mushrooms
1/2 cup chopped sweet red pepper
1 tbsp low-sodium soy sauce
1 tbsp hoisin sauce
1 tbsp water
2 tsp finely chopped garlic
2 tsp finely chopped gingerroot
2 tsp sesame oil
2 tsp rice wine vinegar

6 skin-on salmon fillets (about 4 oz each)
2 tbsp toasted sesame seeds

GARNISH
1/4 cup chopped fresh coriander

1. To make sauce: In a nonstick skillet sprayed with cooking spray, heat oil over medium-high heat; cook onions for 3 minutes or until soft. Stir in mushrooms and peppers; cook for 5 minutes or until vegetables are soft. Stir in remaining sauce ingredients; simmer for 1 minute.
2. Meanwhile, spray salmon with cooking spray; sprinkle with sesame seeds. Either on a barbecue or in a nonstick grill pan sprayed with cooking spray, cook fish over medium-high heat for 5 minutes per side or until fish is just cooked. Place on a serving dish; pour sauce over top. Garnish with coriander.

PREP: About 15 mins.
COOK: About 15 to 18 mins.

MAKES 6 SERVINGS

MAKE AHEAD
Sauce can be made up to 2 days in advance. Cooked fish and sauce can be frozen together for up to 2 weeks.

NUTRITIONAL ANALYSIS
PER SERVING
276 calories
25.4 g protein
13.4 g fat, total
2.8 g fat, saturated
6.8 g carbohydrates
210 mg sodium
75 mg cholesterol
1.9 g fibre

TIP
Another method of cooking this salmon dish is to pour the sauce over top and bake at 425°F for 10 minutes per inch thickness of fish.

seafood louis

This is actually a seafood salad that can be either a first or main course. You can serve it at room temperature or chilled. Both ways, it's delicious. You can use other fish of your choice if shellfish is not your preference. Salmon or tuna work well in this delicious recipe.

8 oz deveined peeled shrimp

8 oz scallops

8 oz surimi or cooked crabmeat

3/4 cup chopped sweet red peppers

1/2 cup chopped sweet green peppers

1/2 cup chopped green onions

1/4 cup sweet chili sauce

3 tbsp light mayonnaise

2 tbsp fresh lemon juice

1/2 tsp Dijon mustard

1/8 tsp each salt and freshly ground black pepper

1/4 cup chopped parsley or dill

1. In a nonstick skillet sprayed with cooking spray, cook shrimp and scallops over medium-high heat for 3 minutes or until cooked through. Cool.
2. Chop shrimp, scallops, and surimi. Place in a bowl. Stir in remaining ingredients.

super quick

PREP: About 15 mins.

COOK: About 3 mins.

MAKES 4 SERVINGS

MAKE AHEAD

Freeze for up to 2 weeks.

NUTRITIONAL ANALYSIS
PER SERVING

226 calories

26 g protein

5.5 g fat, total

0.9 g fat, saturated

18 g carbohydrates

940 mg sodium

115 mg cholesterol

1.3 g fibre

TIPS

If you want to cut back on sodium, eat fresh fish as opposed to seafood. Surimi (imitation crab) contains a fair amount of sodium, but real crabmeat contains much less. Be sure to use sweet chili sauce, which is different from the hot spicy variety.

PREP: About 15 mins.
COOK: About 5 mins.

MAKES 4 SERVINGS

MAKE AHEAD
Salsa can be made up to
1 day in advance.

NUTRITIONAL ANALYSIS
PER SERVING
185 calories
20 g protein
4 g fat, total
0.6 g fat, saturated
10.5 g carbohydrates
175 mg sodium
150 mg cholesterol
1.2 g fibre

TIPS
Prepare the salsa a couple of
hours ahead to let the flavors
blend. Don't overcook the
shrimp or they become
rubbery.

shrimp with pineapple salsa

Forget heavy butter and cream sauces—salsas are the greatest way to liven up a main meal. Pineapple is outstanding when in season. Feel free to use any other fruit in season, such as Asian pears, mangoes, or kiwis, but do not use canned pineapple since it is watery and doesn't have the intense flavor of fresh pineapple.

SALSA
1-1/4 cup finely diced fresh pineapple
1/2 cup finely diced sweet red peppers
1/3 cup finely diced sweet onions
1/3 cup chopped coriander or parsley
2 tbsp apricot or peach jam
2 tbsp fresh lemon juice
2 tsp sesame oil
1 tsp minced garlic
1/2 tsp hot pepper sauce

1 lb deveined peeled shrimp

GARNISH
2 tbsp chopped fresh coriander

1. To make salsa: In a bowl, stir salsa ingredients together.
2. In a nonstick skillet sprayed with cooking spray, cook shrimp on medium-high heat just until cooked, about 3 to 5 minutes.
3. Serve shrimp with salsa alongside, garnished with coriander.

shrimp cakes with roasted red pepper sauce

The combination of shrimp and sweet red pepper sauce is wonderful. These shrimp cakes are also elegant enough to serve as appetizers.

SAUCE
1 sweet red pepper, halved, seeds and ribs removed
2 tsp vegetable oil
2 tsp light mayonnaise

SHRIMP CAKES
1 lb deveined peeled shrimp
2/3 cup chopped sweet red peppers
1/3 cup chopped green onions
1/3 cup seasoned bread crumbs
1/3 cup chopped fresh dill
3 tbsp light mayonnaise
2 tbsp fresh lemon juice
1 tsp minced garlic
1/8 tsp each salt and freshly ground black pepper

2 tsp vegetable oil

1. Preheat oven to 450°F. Spray rimmed baking sheet with cooking spray.
2. To make sauce: Place red pepper halves on prepared baking sheet. Roast in centre of oven for 20 to 25 minutes or until charred and soft. Place peppers in a bowl, cover with plastic wrap, and let cool. Peel peppers. Place in a food processor along with vegetable oil and mayonnaise; purée until smooth. Using a rubber spatula, transfer pepper mixture to a serving bowl.
3. To make shrimp cakes: Place ingredients in the food processor. Pulse on and off just until ingredients are combined but mixture is still coarse. Form shrimp mixture into 8 cakes.
4. In a large nonstick skillet sprayed with cooking spray, heat oil over medium-high heat; cook cakes for 8 minutes, turning once, or until browned on both sides. Place on a serving dish. Serve with sauce.

PREP: About 15 mins.
COOK: About 30 mins.

MAKES 8 CAKES

MAKE AHEAD
Sauce can be made up to 3 days in advance and frozen for up to 2 months. The shrimp cakes can be prepared up to 1 day in advance. Cooked cakes can be frozen for up to 1 month.

NUTRITIONAL ANALYSIS PER SERVING
132 calories
12.6 g protein
5.8 g fat, total
0.9 g fat, saturated
7.4 g carbohydrates
292 mg sodium
88.5 mg cholesterol
1 g fibre

TIPS
For a variation, try making this recipe with crabmeat or surimi (imitation crabmeat). You can always use bottled roasted sweet peppers packed in water if you don't have time to roast your own.

PREP: About 5 mins.
COOK: About 5 mins.

MAKES 4 SERVINGS

MAKE AHEAD
Cook mussels only when you are ready to serve them unless serving at room temperature: if so, prepare them up to 1 day early.

NUTRITIONAL ANALYSIS
PER SERVING
290 calories
30.7 g protein
9.4 g fat, total
1.6 g fat, saturated
20.6 g carbohydrates
525 mg sodium
65 mg cholesterol
2.2 g fibre

TIP
If the mussels are cracked or don't open after cooking, toss them out.

mussels with creamy tomato sauce

Fresh mussels are a real treat to serve at home. But so often we are uncertain how to cook them and what sauce to serve with them. This is a great, easy recipe that has lots of flavor and goes well with French or Italian bread.

2 tsp vegetable oil
1 cup diced onions
2 tsp finely chopped garlic
1 cup tomato pasta sauce
1/3 cup fish stock or wine
1/3 cup 2% evaporated milk
2 lb cleaned mussels

GARNISH
1/4 cup chopped fresh basil

1. In a nonstick skillet sprayed with cooking spray, heat oil over medium-high heat; cook onions and garlic for 5 minutes or until onion begins to brown. Add remaining ingredients, except basil. Cover, and simmer just until mussels are opened, about 5 minutes. Discard any mussels that do not open. Sprinkle with basil.

vegetarian main dishes

potato vegetable quiche

PREP: About 20 mins.
COOK: About 65 mins.

MAKES 8 SERVINGS

MAKE AHEAD
Prepare crust and filling early
in the day, but don't combine
until ready to bake. Freeze for
up to 1 month.

NUTRITIONAL ANALYSIS
PER SERVING
187 calories
8.8 g protein
7.4 g fat, total
2.7 g fat, saturated
21.2 g carbohydrates
181 mg sodium
61 mg cholesterol
2.7 g fibre

Forget butter- or lard-based quiche crust, which is too high in calories and fat (the quiche filling rarely puts the calorie count over the top). My crust for this quiche is made of flavorful mashed potatoes.

CRUST
2 medium Yukon Gold potatoes
    (about 1 lb), peeled and cubed
1/2 cup all-purpose flour
3 tbsp low-fat milk
2 tbsp grated Parmesan cheese
1 tbsp olive oil
1 tsp minced garlic
1/4 tsp each salt and freshly
    ground black pepper

TOPPING
2 oz goat cheese, crumbled
3 tbsp grated Parmesan cheese

FILLING
(prepare filling while baking crust)
2 tsp vegetable oil
1 cup chopped onions
2 tsp minced garlic
2 cups chopped broccoli
3/4 cup chopped sweet red peppers
1 tsp dried basil
1/2 tsp dried oregano
2 eggs
3/4 cup low-fat milk
1 tsp Dijon mustard

1. Preheat oven to 375°F. Spray a 9-inch pie pan with cooking spray.
2. To make crust: Place potatoes in a saucepan and add cold water to cover. Bring to a boil; cook for 15 to 20 minutes or until tender when pierced with the tip of a sharp knife. Drain. Add remaining crust ingredients to potatoes and mash thoroughly. Pat potato mixture into the bottom and sides of prepared pie pan. Bake in centre of oven for 25 minutes. Remove from oven, leaving heat on.
3. To make filling: Meanwhile, in a nonstick skillet, heat oil over medium heat. Cook onions and garlic for 5 minutes or until onion begins to brown. Stir in broccoli, peppers, basil, and oregano; cook another 5 minutes or just until broccoli begins to turn bright green. Remove from heat. Stir in eggs, milk, and mustard. Spoon vegetable mixture into warm potato crust. Sprinkle with cheeses.
4. Bake in centre of oven for 25 minutes or just until centre is set.

pesto rosti potato pizza

The Mövenpick restaurant chain is famous for its rosti potatoes, which are made with lots of oil. Here's my lower-fat version flavored with pesto and made with much less oil.

3 medium Yukon Gold potatoes (about 1-1/2 lb), peeled
1/2 tsp salt
1/4 tsp pepper
2 tsp butter, margarine, or vegetable oil
2 tbsp Rose's Light Pesto (see page 184) or store-bought
3 tbsp chopped green onions
3 tbsp finely chopped sweet red peppers
2 tbsp chopped black olives
1 oz goat cheese, crumbled

1. Shred potatoes. In a bowl, stir together potatoes, salt, and pepper. In a 9-inch nonstick skillet sprayed with cooking spray, melt butter over medium heat. Place potato mixture in skillet; pat down with a spatula. Cook potatoes over medium-low heat for 8 minutes or until bottom is brown.
2. Carefully slide potatoes onto a large plate and invert back into skillet. Cook another 5 minutes; spread pesto over top. Sprinkle with remaining ingredients. Cover, reduce heat to low, and cook another 3 to 5 minutes or until goat cheese begins to melt. Slide onto serving dish.

PREP: About 10 mins.
COOK: About 18 mins.

MAKES 6 SERVINGS

MAKE AHEAD
You can grate the potatoes ahead of time, but place them in cold water to prevent browning. Before using, drain the potatoes and squeeze dry.

NUTRITIONAL ANALYSIS PER SERVING
175 calories
3.3 g protein
5.4 g fat, total
2.4 g fat, saturated
13.8 g carbohydrates
280 mg sodium
8 mg cholesterol
1.6 g fibre

TIP
Using the right attachment on my food processor, I can grate the potatoes for this recipe in less than a minute.

goat cheese potato gratin

PREP: About 15 mins.
COOK: About 35 mins.

MAKES 8 SERVINGS

MAKE AHEAD
This can be prepared up to
1 day in advance and baked
just before serving.

NUTRITIONAL ANALYSIS
PER SERVING
197 calories
7.4 g protein
5.7 g fat, total
2.3 g fat, saturated
29 g carbohydrates
202 mg sodium
8 mg cholesterol
3 g fibre

Traditional potato gratin is extremely high in fat and calories due to the excess butter, cheese, and cream. The potatoes absorb all the fat. This variation uses evaporated milk instead of butter and cream.

3 medium Yukon Gold potatoes (about
   1-1/2 lb), unpeeled and scrubbed (boil
   potatoes while sautéing vegetables)
2 tsp vegetable oil
1 cup chopped onions
1/2 cup chopped sweet red peppers
2 tsp minced garlic
1 tsp dried basil
3/4 cup 2% evaporated milk
3/4 cup vegetable stock

2 tbsp all-purpose flour
1 tsp Dijon mustard
2 oz goat cheese, crumbled
2 tbsp grated Parmesan cheese
2 tbsp Rose's Light Pesto (see page 184) or
   store-bought
1/4 tsp each salt and freshly ground
   black pepper

GARNISH
2 tbsp chopped fresh basil or parsley

1. Preheat oven to 375°F. Spray a 13- × 9-inch glass baking dish with cooking spray.

2. Place potatoes in saucepan and add cold water to cover. Bring to a boil; cook for 15 to 20 minutes or until just tender when pierced with the tip of a sharp knife. Do not cook right through. Drain. Cool.

3. In a nonstick skillet, heat oil over medium heat. Cook peppers, onions, garlic, and dried basil for 5 minutes or just until onions begin to brown. Remove from heat.

4. Slice cooled potatoes into 1/2-inch thick slices widthwise; lay out in prepared baking dish, overlapping if necessary. Spread onion mixture over top.

5. In a saucepan, whisk together milk, stock, flour, and mustard until flour is dissolved. Place over medium heat and bring to a simmer, stirring; cook just until slightly thickened, about 3 minutes. Remove from heat and stir in remaining ingredients, except chopped basil. Pour milk mixture over potato mixture.

6. Bake uncovered in centre of oven for 20 minutes or just until potatoes are tender. Serve sprinkled with basil.

greek-style creamy potato strudel

Mashed Yukon Gold potatoes with cheese, sautéed onions, and sun-dried tomatoes go beautifully with phyllo. The Yukon Gold potato has a creamier, more buttery texture than the basic white potato.

FILLING

2 tsp vegetable oil

1/2 cup chopped onions

1 tsp minced garlic

1 medium Yukon Gold potato (about 8 oz), peeled and quartered

1/3 cup low-fat sour cream

1/4 cup chopped rehydrated sun-dried tomatoes

3 tbsp chopped green onions

2 oz light feta cheese, crumbled

1/8 tsp each salt and freshly ground black pepper

6 sheets phyllo pastry

1. Preheat oven to 375°F. Spray a baking sheet with cooking spray.
2. To make filling: In a nonstick skillet sprayed with cooking spray, heat oil over medium heat. Cook onions and garlic for 3 minutes or until golden. Remove from heat.
3. Place potatoes in saucepan and add cold water to cover. Bring to a boil; cook for 20 minutes or until tender when pierced with the tip of a sharp knife. Drain. In a bowl, mash potatoes with the onion mixture. Stir in remaining filling ingredients.
4. Keeping the remaining phyllo covered with a cloth to prevent drying out, layer 2 sheets of phyllo one on top of the other. Spray with cooking spray. Layer remaining sheets on top, spraying every other sheet. Spread potato mixture over phyllo, leaving a 1-inch border bare around the edges. (Wet a knife to spread the potato mixture easily.) Starting from the long end, roll several times. Tuck in the short ends and continue to roll. Place phyllo packet on prepared baking sheet. Spray with cooking spray.
5. Bake in centre of oven for 25 to 30 minutes or until golden.

PREP: About 10 mins.
COOK: About 45 mins.

MAKES 8 SERVINGS

MAKE AHEAD
Prepare the filling up to 1 day in advance or the entire roll early in the day, keeping roll well covered until ready to bake. Leftovers can be frozen for up to 2 months and reheated in a 350°F oven for 10 minutes.

NUTRITIONAL ANALYSIS PER SERVING

130 calories

4 g protein

4.2 g fat, total

1.5 g fat, saturated

19 g carbohydrates

270 mg sodium

5.9 mg cholesterol

1.3 g fibre

TIPS
Never try to mash potatoes in a food processor or they'll get gluey in texture. I use a good old-fashioned potato masher. A hand beater makes them even fluffier.

polenta with goat cheese and roasted vegetables

Homemade polenta always tastes better than the store-bought version and takes only 5 minutes to cook. Keep the heat low when cooking or the polenta will bubble out of the pan! The roasted vegetables are sensational with this firm polenta.

PREP: About 10 mins.
COOK: About 40 mins.

MAKES 4 SERVINGS

MAKE AHEAD
Grill these vegetables up to
1 day in advance; refrigerate
and reheat when serving the
polenta. The polenta can also
be made 1 day in advance;
gently reheat either in the
microwave for 30 seconds on
High or in a 350°F oven for
5 minutes.

NUTRITIONAL ANALYSIS
PER SERVING
253 calories
7.8 g protein
7.8 g fat, total
2.7 g fat, saturated
38 g carbohydrates
264 mg sodium
6.5 mg cholesterol
4.4 g fibre

TIPS
Feel free to select other vegetables to roast. You can add
garlic, Parmesan cheese, or
dried herbs to the polenta
while cooking it.

POLENTA
3 cups vegetable stock
1 cup finely ground cornmeal

1 tbsp olive oil
2 tsp balsamic vinegar

GARNISH
2 oz goat cheese, crumbled

VEGETABLES
1 small head garlic
1 sweet red pepper, cut into quarters
1 sweet yellow pepper, cut into quarters
1 medium red onion, sliced
2 small zucchini (about 8 oz), cut in half lengthwise

1. Preheat oven to 425°F. Spray an 8-inch square glass baking dish with cooking spray. Line a rimmed baking sheet with foil; spray with cooking spray.
2. To make polenta: In a deep saucepan set over medium-high heat, bring stock to a boil. Reduce heat to low; gradually whisk in cornmeal. Cook, stirring constantly, for 5 minutes. Pour into prepared baking dish, smoothing top; chill.
3. To make vegetables: Cut 1/2-inch from top of garlic head to expose cloves. Wrap garlic head loosely in foil; place on prepared baking sheet. Add remaining vegetables. Spray with cooking spray. Roast garlic and vegetables, turning occasionally, for 40 minutes or until tender. Squeeze garlic out of skins; chop remaining vegetables. Transfer all to a bowl. Sprinkle with olive oil and balsamic vinegar; toss to coat well.
4. Turn polenta onto a cutting board; cut into 4 squares. In a large nonstick skillet sprayed with cooking spray, cook polenta over medium-high heat for 2 minutes or until golden. Turn; cook for 1 minute. Place polenta on serving plates. Top polenta with the vegetable mixture. Serve sprinkled with goat cheese.

stuffed zucchini

This stuffed zucchini dish works as a lunch, a side vegetable dish, or an appetizer. The sautéed onions and zucchini pulp combined with the cheese, sun-dried tomato, and olive stuffing are delicious.

2 large zucchini (about 1 lb), sliced lengthwise in half
1/2 cup smooth light ricotta cheese
1 oz light cream cheese
1/4 cup chopped rehydrated sun-dried tomatoes
1/4 cup chopped fresh parsley
3 tbsp diced black olives
2 tbsp grated Parmesan cheese
1 tsp vegetable oil
1/2 cup chopped sweet onions
1 tsp minced garlic
2 tbsp toasted pine nuts
1 tbsp grated Parmesan cheese

1. Preheat oven to 400°F.
2. Place zucchini halves on a rimmed baking sheet; bake for 10 minutes. Scoop out most of flesh, leaving a 1/2-inch thickness attached to the skin. Chop scooped-out flesh. Set aside 1/2 cup. Save remaining zucchini pulp for another use or discard. Place zucchini "boats" on a baking sheet.
3. In a food processor or blender, combine ricotta, cream cheese, sun-dried tomatoes, parsley, black olives, and Parmesan until well mixed. Do not purée.
4. In a nonstick skillet, heat oil over medium-high heat. Cook onions and garlic for 3 minutes or until softened. Stir in reserved 1/2 cup zucchini pulp; cook for 3 minutes longer or until zucchini and onions are tender. Stir into ricotta mixture. Divide mixture among zucchini boats. Sprinkle evenly with pine nuts and Parmesan.
5. Bake in centre of oven for 10 minutes or until heated through. Cut boats in half before serving.

PREP: About 15 mins.
COOK: About 25 mins.

MAKES 8 SERVINGS

MAKE AHEAD
Prepare stuffing up to 3 days before or the entire dish up to 1 day in advance. Bake just before serving. Reheat leftovers in 350°F oven for 5 minutes. Freeze for up to 2 weeks.

NUTRITIONAL ANALYSIS
PER SERVING
80 calories
4.2 g protein
4.5 g fat, total
1.5 g fat, saturated
5 g carbohydrates
250 mg sodium
8 mg cholesterol
1.2 g fibre

TIPS
To rehydrate sun-dried tomatoes, soak in boiling water for 15 minutes or cover with water and microwave for 1 minute.

super quick

PREP: About 10 mins.
COOK: About 6 mins.

MAKES 4 SERVINGS

MAKE AHEAD
These can be prepared 1 day in advance and cooked just before serving. Alternatively, cook patties up to 1 day in advance and reheat gently in the microwave or in a 400°F oven for 5 minutes. Cooked burgers can be frozen for up to 2 months. Warm gently over medium heat.

NUTRITIONAL ANALYSIS
PER BURGER
231 calories
10 g protein
7.4 g fat, total
2.1 g fat, saturated
31 g carbohydrates
510 mg sodium
62 mg cholesterol
5 g fibre

TIPS
Instead of carrots, try using shredded zucchini or sweet potato, and feel free to substitute black beans or white kidney beans for the chick-peas.

veggie burgers

Veggie burgers have become a trendy alternative to hamburgers at many fast-food outlets. But be aware that these burgers often are fried and made with a lot of fillers, which add unnecessary calories and fat. In the end, a hamburger may contain fewer calories than a fried veggie burger. This homemade version is delicious and low in fat and calories. I like to serve these burgers on a bun or in a pita with all the usual garnishes—tomatoes, onions, and lettuce.

BURGERS
3 medium carrots, shredded
1 cup rinsed and drained canned chick-peas
3/4 cup dry seasoned bread crumbs
1/3 cup shredded light Cheddar cheese
1/3 cup chopped fresh coriander or parsley
1/4 cup chopped green onions
1 egg
2 tbsp fresh lemon juice
2 tsp low-sodium soy sauce
1 tsp minced garlic
2 tsp vegetable oil

SAUCE
1/4 cup low-fat sour cream
1 tsp Dijon mustard

1. To make burgers: In a food processor, combine all burger ingredients except the oil; pulse processor on and off until ingredients are well mixed. Form into 4 patties, each about 1/3 cup. In a large nonstick skillet sprayed with cooking spray, heat oil over medium heat. Cook burgers for 3 minutes per side or until golden on both sides.
2. To make sauce: In a small bowl, stir together sour cream and mustard. Serve burgers with a dollop of sauce.

spinach and feta phyllo pie

This is like a large spanakopita, except it's baked in a pie plate. Serve this phyllo pie with a large green salad.

FILLING

2 tsp vegetable oil

1 cup finely chopped onions

2 tsp minced garlic

1 pkg (10 oz) frozen spinach, thawed, drained, chopped, and squeezed dry

1 tsp dried oregano

1/4 tsp each salt and freshly ground black pepper

2 oz light feta cheese, crumbled

1/2 cup shredded low-fat mozzarella cheese

1/3 cup chopped fresh dill or parsley

1/3 cup chopped green onions

1/4 cup chopped black olives

2 tbsp dry seasoned bread crumbs

1 egg

6 sheets phyllo pastry

1. Preheat oven to 375°F. Spray a 9-inch pie pan with cooking spray.
2. To make filling: In a nonstick skillet sprayed with cooking spray, heat oil over medium heat. Cook onions and garlic for 5 minutes or just until onions begin to brown. Stir in spinach, oregano, and salt and pepper; cook for 3 minutes. Remove from heat. Stir in remaining filling ingredients.
3. Keeping remaining phyllo covered with a cloth to prevent drying out, layer 2 sheets of phyllo in prepared pie pan, leaving edges hanging over side of pan. Spray with cooking spray. Layer remaining sheets on top, spraying every other sheet. Spoon filling into pan and fold phyllo over top to enclose.
4. Bake in centre of oven for 15 to 20 minutes or until phyllo is golden.

PREP: About 15 mins.
COOK: About 25 mins.

MAKES 6 SERVINGS

MAKE AHEAD
The filling can be prepared up to 2 days in advance. It's best to bake just before serving to keep phyllo crisp. Reheat by placing in a 350°F oven for 10 minutes.

NUTRITIONAL ANALYSIS PER SERVING
189 calories
8.7 g protein
8.2 g fat, total
3.2 g fat, saturated
20.2 g carbohydrates
567 mg sodium
49 mg cholesterol
3.2 g fibre

TIPS
When preparing phyllo pastry, keep sheets that you are not working with covered with a tea towel; phyllo quickly dries out and can crumble. You can refreeze any phyllo not used by rolling it up and wrapping in plastic wrap. Never thaw phyllo in the microwave.

mushroom strudel

PREP: About 10 mins.
COOK: About 40 mins.

MAKES 8 SERVINGS

MAKE AHEAD

Prepare entire phyllo filling up to 2 days in advance. It's always better to fill and bake phyllo just before serving. If necessary, strudel can be prepared and frozen for up to 1 month. Bake frozen at 350°F, adding 10 extra minutes to the baking time.

NUTRITIONAL ANALYSIS
PER SERVING

159 calories

8.6 g protein

7.2 g fat, total

2.8 g fat, saturated

15 g carbohydrates

256 mg sodium

12 mg cholesterol

2.1 g fibre

TIPS

Be sure to sauté mushrooms on high heat to rid them of excess moisture. Regular mushrooms have more moisture than wild ones.

If you love mushrooms, you'll get your fill with this strudel. Six cups of meaty oyster mushrooms, mixed with cheese, black olives, and dill, are wonderful in this roll. Use whichever variety of mushrooms you prefer.

FILLING

2 tsp vegetable oil

1 cup chopped onions

2 tsp minced garlic

6 cups sliced oyster mushrooms (about 1 lb)

1/4 cup vegetable stock

1 tsp dried thyme leaves

3/4 cup smooth light ricotta cheese

2 oz goat cheese

1/3 cup low-fat milk

1/3 cup chopped fresh dill

1/4 cup sliced black olives

2 tbsp grated Parmesan cheese

1/8 tsp each salt and freshly ground black pepper

6 sheets phyllo pastry

1. Preheat oven to 375°F. Spray a baking sheet with cooking spray.

2. To make filling: In a large nonstick skillet sprayed with cooking spray, heat oil over medium-high heat. Cook onions and garlic for 4 minutes or until softened. Stir in mushrooms, stock, and thyme; cook for 8 to 10 minutes, stirring frequently, or until mushrooms are tender and most of liquid is absorbed. Transfer to a bowl. Cool for 5 minutes. Stir remaining filling ingredients into cooled mushroom mixture.

3. Keeping remaining phyllo covered with a cloth to prevent drying out, layer 2 sheets of phyllo one on top of the other. Spray with cooking spray. Layer remaining sheets on top, spraying every other sheet. Spread filling over phyllo, leaving a 2-inch border bare around the edges. Starting from the long end, roll several times. Tuck in the short ends and continue to roll. Place on prepared baking sheet. Spray with cooking spray.

4. Bake in centre of oven for 25 to 30 minutes or until golden.

vegetable nachos with cheese, sour cream, and salsa

The first time I served this to company was during the tennis finals of the U.S. Open. Everyone thought this nacho-type dish was made with ground beef! It's delicious served as an informal appetizer or just as a snack. Use only baked tortilla chips since the regular ones are fried and contain six times the fat!

6 oz soy-based ground beef substitute
3/4 cup salsa
4 cups baked tortilla chips (about 5 oz)
1/2 cup shredded low-fat Cheddar cheese
1/4 cup sliced black or green olives

GARNISH
1/4 cup chopped green onions
1/2 cup salsa
1/4 cup low-fat sour cream

1. Preheat oven to 425°F.
2. In a bowl, stir together ground soy and salsa. On a rimmed baking sheet, pile half of the tortilla chips; top with half of the ground soy mixture. Sprinkle with half the cheese and then half the olives. Repeat layers.
3. Bake in centre of oven for 5 to 8 minutes or until cheese is melted.
4. Sprinkle with green onions. Serve with salsa and sour cream.

super quick

PREP: About 10 mins.
COOK: About 8 mins.

MAKES 4 SERVINGS

MAKE AHEAD
To preserve the crispness of the tortilla chips, it's best to prepare nachos just before baking them.

NUTRITIONAL ANALYSIS PER SERVING
260 calories
16 g protein
4.9 g fat, total
1.4 g fat, saturated
38 g carbohydrates
758 mg sodium
8 mg cholesterol
5.2 g fibre

TIPS
Get all the ingredients ready in advance, but don't sprinkle them on the chips until ready to bake or the chips will get soggy. For the best taste, serve immediately from the oven.

southwest tortilla bake

With the beans, tortillas, cheese, and vegetables, this is a nutrition-packed meal that tastes delicious and looks beautiful when served.

4 large flavored tortillas

2 tsp vegetable oil
1 cup chopped onions
2 tsp minced garlic
1 cup chopped sweet green peppers
1 cup drained canned corn
1 cup medium salsa
1 tsp dried oregano
1/2 tsp cumin

1 cup shredded low-fat mozzarella cheese
1/2 cup light ricotta cheese
2 oz light cream cheese, softened
1/3 cup light sour cream

2 cups rinsed and drained canned red kidney beans, mashed

1. Preheat oven to 375°F.
2. Trim tortillas to a fit 9-inch springform pan. Set aside.
3. In a nonstick skillet sprayed with cooking spray, heat oil over medium-high heat; cook onions and garlic for 5 minutes or until onions are lightly browned. Stir in green peppers and corn; cook for 8 minutes, stirring constantly, or until corn begins to char. Stir in salsa, oregano, and cumin. Remove from heat.
4. In a bowl, stir together cheeses and sour cream.
5. Place 1 tortilla in the springform pan. Spread with one-third of salsa mixture, one-third of beans, and one-third of cheese mixture; top with another tortilla. Repeat layers twice. Cover with foil.
6. Bake in centre of oven for 20 to 25 minutes or until hot.

PREP: About 15 mins.
COOK: About 35 mins.

MAKES 8 SERVINGS

MAKE AHEAD
Prepare entire tortilla bake up to 1 day in advance. It can be frozen for up to 2 months. Defrost, then bake.

NUTRITIONAL ANALYSIS PER SERVING
287 calories
15 g protein
8.3 g fat, total
3.7 g fat, saturated
38 g carbohydrates
451 mg sodium
19 mg cholesterol
7.6 g fibre

TIPS
Leftover beans can be frozen for up to 2 months. For convenience, keep frozen blocks of cheese available, let come to room temperature, and grate in a food processor. Keep grated cheese in containers in refrigerator for later use.

tofu and red kidney bean chili

Chili made with tofu is much better for you nutritionally than the meat version. Usually, chili is made from regular ground beef, which has 38 percent fat. Tofu, a soy-based product, may protect both our hearts and bones and even reduce the risk of prostate and breast cancer. Try serving this chili over rice, pasta, couscous, or the ancient grains such as quinoa, millet, or wheatberries.

8 oz firm tofu, cubed

1 tsp vegetable oil

1 cup chopped onions

1 cup chopped sweet green peppers

1 cup chopped carrots

2 tsp minced garlic

1 cup chopped zucchini

1 tbsp chili powder

1 tsp dried basil

1 tsp dried oregano

2 cans (each 19 oz) whole tomatoes, crushed

1 tbsp tomato paste

2 tsp packed brown sugar

1/2 tsp salt

1/4 tsp freshly ground black pepper

2 cups rinsed and drained canned red kidney beans

GARNISH
3 tbsp chopped parsley

1. In a nonstick skillet sprayed with cooking spray, cook tofu over medium-high heat for 5 minutes, turning, until browned on all sides. Set aside.

2. In a large nonstick saucepan, heat oil over medium heat. Cook onions, green peppers, carrots, and garlic for 8 minutes or until onions are softened. Stir in zucchini, chili powder, basil, and oregano; cook for 2 minutes longer. Stir in tomatoes, tomato paste, brown sugar, salt, and pepper. Bring to a boil. Reduce heat to medium-low; stir in kidney beans and tofu. Cover, and cook mixture for 35 minutes or until thickened and carrots are tender. Garnish with parsley.

PREP: About 15 mins.
COOK: About 45 mins.

MAKES 6 SERVINGS

MAKE AHEAD
This dish can be cooked and either frozen for up to 2 months or refrigerated for up to 3 days.

NUTRITIONAL ANALYSIS PER SERVING
234 calories
14 g protein
5.1 g fat, total
0.6 g fat, saturated
33 g carbohydrates
712 mg sodium
0 mg cholesterol
11 g fibre

TIPS
Remember to use firm tofu, since soft tofu will fall apart. If you want a spicier chili, try adding 1 tsp freshly minced jalapeño peppers or some hot sauce.

soy- and cheese-stuffed manicotti

PREP: About 15 mins.
COOK: About 23 mins.

MAKES 5 SERVINGS

MAKE AHEAD
Prepare this up to 1 day in
advance but bake just before
serving. Uncooked, this dish
can be frozen for up to
2 months. If frozen, add
15 minutes to baking time.

NUTRITIONAL ANALYSIS
PER SERVING
251 calories
18 g protein
6.9 g fat, total
2.4 g fat, saturated
30 g carbohydrates
580 mg sodium
52 mg cholesterol
4.4 g fibre

TIPS
When buying ground soy,
choose the Italian-spiced one,
which is more flavorful than
the regular version.

One of my previous books had a recipe similar to this one, except it contained ground beef, which is extremely high in fat and calories. I serve this dish to all my "carnivore" friends and family, and not one has guessed it is made with soy!

10 manicotti shells

FILLING
2 tsp vegetable oil
1/2 cup diced onions
1-1/2 tsp minced garlic
1/2 tsp dried basil
1/8 tsp each salt and pepper
6 oz soy-based ground beef substitute
1/3 cup vegetable stock
1 tbsp tomato paste
3/4 cup smooth light ricotta cheese
1 oz light cream cheese
3 tbsp grated Parmesan cheese

1 cup tomato pasta sauce

1. Preheat oven to 375°F. Spray a 9-inch glass baking dish with cooking spray.
2. In a large pot of boiling water, cook manicotti shells according to package instructions or until tender. Drain, cover, and set aside.
3. To make filling: In a nonstick skillet, heat oil over medium-high heat. Cook onions and garlic for 5 minutes or until vegetables are softened; add basil and salt and pepper. Stir in ground soy, stock, and tomato paste; cook for 2 minutes. Remove from heat. Stir in ricotta, cream cheese, and 2 tbsp of the Parmesan. Place approximately 1/4 cup filling into each manicotti shell. Pour 3/4 cup of the tomato sauce into prepared pan. Add filled manicotti; pour remaining sauce over top. Sprinkle with remaining Parmesan cheese. Cover pan with foil.
4. Bake in centre of oven for 15 minutes or until hot.

tofu satays with hoisin sesame sauce

I love chicken, beef, and shrimp satays, but if you're a vegetarian or you just want a healthier alternative, try these tofu satays. Tofu absorbs whatever flavors it's cooked with.

1 large sweet green pepper, cut into 16 squares
1 large sweet red pepper, cut into 16 squares
1/2 sweet onion, cut into 16 pieces
12 oz firm tofu, cut into 16 cubes 2- × 2-inch

SAUCE
1/4 cup hoisin sauce
1/4 cup packed brown sugar
5 tsp black bean sauce
5 tsp low-sodium soy sauce
1 tbsp sesame oil
1-1/2 tsp minced garlic
1-1/2 tsp minced gingerroot

GARNISH
1/4 cup chopped fresh coriander or parsley

1. Thread peppers, onions, and tofu alternately on 4 long or 8 short wooden or metal skewers, dividing the vegetables evenly among them.
2. To make sauce: In a bowl, stir sauce ingredients together until smooth.
3. On a preheated barbecue or in a nonstick grill pan sprayed with cooking spray, cook tofu satays over medium heat for 10 minutes, turning occasionally, or until browned on all sides. Brush half of sauce over satays; continue cooking another 10 minutes, turning occasionally, or just until vegetables are soft and grilled. Serve with remaining sauce, garnished with coriander.

PREP: About 15 mins.
COOK: About 20 mins.

MAKES 4 SERVINGS

MAKE AHEAD
The sauce can be prepared and refrigerated for up to 1 week or frozen for up to 2 months. The tofu satays can be cooked up to 1 day in advance and gently reheated before serving.

NUTRITIONAL ANALYSIS PER SERVING
240 calories
9.9 g protein
7 g fat, total
1 g fat, saturated
38.7 g carbohydrates
601 mg sodium
0.5 mg cholesterol
5.3 g fibre

TIPS
Be sure to buy firm tofu: the medium textured tofu is too soft and the extra firm too tough. Once opened, cover unused tofu with water in a container and refrigerate.

super quick

PREP: About 5 mins.
COOK: About 10 mins.

MAKES 4 SERVINGS

MAKE AHEAD
Prepare the entire dish up to
1 day in advance, but bake
just before serving.

NUTRITIONAL ANALYSIS
PER SERVING
260 calories
15 g protein
10 g fat, total
3.1 g fat, saturated
12 g carbohydrates
570 mg sodium
64 mg cholesterol
1.5 g fibre

TIPS
It's important to buy firm tofu,
but not the extra-firm product,
which is too tough. Softer
tofu will fall apart.

tofu parmesan

Forget eggplant or chicken Parmesan! This dish is a terrific, healthy alternative to those old favorites.

1/2 cup seasoned bread crumbs
1 tbsp grated Parmesan cheese
1 egg
2 tbsp water
1 lb firm tofu, sliced horizontally into 1-inch slices
2 tsp vegetable oil
3/4 cup tomato pasta sauce
1/2 tsp dried basil
1/2 cup shredded low-fat mozzarella cheese

1. Preheat oven to 425°F.
2. On a plate, stir together bread crumbs and Parmesan. In a shallow bowl, whisk together egg and water. Dip tofu slices into egg mixture; coat tofu with breadcrumb mixture.
3. In a large nonstick skillet sprayed with cooking spray, heat oil over medium heat. Cook tofu for 5 minutes, turning once, or until browned on both sides.
4. Mix tomato sauce with basil. Spread half of tomato sauce over bottom of a 9-inch square baking dish. Lay tofu slices over top; pour remaining sauce over tofu. Sprinkle with mozzarella.
5. Bake in centre of oven for 5 to 8 minutes or just until cheese melts and sauce is warm.

desserts

orange tiramisu

PREP: About 25 mins.
CHILL TIME: About 2 h.

MAKES 12 SERVINGS

MAKE AHEAD
This dessert can be made up to 1 day in advance or early the same day.

NUTRITIONAL ANALYSIS PER SERVING
204 calories
7.8 g protein
6.3 g fat, total
3.4 g fat, saturated
29 g carbohydrates
88 mg cholesterol
0.2 g fibre

TIP
Always keep a container of orange juice concentrate in the freezer, and don't worry if it defrosts: it can always be refrozen.

In previous cookbooks, I've developed recipes for lemon and chocolate tiramisu. This is my orange variation. Although a traditional tiramisu calls for mascarpone (which has more fat than butter or whipping cream), my version uses the lower-fat ricotta cheese.

1-3/4 cups smooth light ricotta cheese
4 oz light cream cheese, softened
3/4 cup plus 1/3 cup granulated sugar
3 tbsp plus 1/4 cup orange juice concentrate, thawed
1 tbsp finely grated orange rind
1 large egg yolk
3 large egg whites
1/4 tsp cream of tartar
1 cup boiling water
20 3-inch ladyfinger cookies

GARNISH
grated orange zest

1. Spray a 9-inch square cake pan or decorative serving dish with cooking spray.
2. In a food processor, purée ricotta cheese, cream cheese, 1/2 cup of the 3/4 cup sugar, 3 tbsp orange juice concentrate, orange rind, and egg yolk until very smooth. Transfer to a large bowl. In another bowl and using an electric mixer, beat egg whites with cream of tartar until foamy. Gradually add 1/3 cup of the sugar, beating until stiff peaks form. Stir one-quarter of egg whites into ricotta mixture. Gently fold in remaining egg whites just until blended.
3. In a bowl, whisk together water, the remaining 1/4 cup sugar and 1/4 cup orange juice concentrate. Dip each ladyfinger in orange juice mixture just enough to moisten. Place half of ladyfingers in bottom of prepared pan. Pour half of ricotta mixture over ladyfingers. Repeat layers. Chill at least 2 hours. Garnish with orange zest.

cashew cream cheese pie

The combination of cheesecake and cashews is too good for words. I like to serve this pie either at room temperature or chilled.

CRUST

1-3/4 cups vanilla wafer crumbs or
    graham cracker crumbs

2 tbsp granulated sugar

2 tbsp water

1 tbsp vegetable oil

CASHEW FILLING

2/3 cup packed brown sugar

1/2 cup chopped toasted cashews

1/2 cup golden corn syrup

1 large egg

2 large egg whites

2 tbsp unsweetened cocoa powder

1 tbsp molasses

CHEESECAKE FILLING

3/4 cup smooth light ricotta cheese

1/3 cup granulated sugar

3 oz cup light cream cheese, softened

1/4 cup low-fat sour cream

1 large egg

1 tbsp all-purpose flour

1 tsp vanilla

1. Preheat oven to 375°F. Spray a 9-inch pie plate with cooking spray.

2. To make crust: In a bowl, stir together crust ingredients until mixture holds together. Press onto bottom and side of prepared pie plate.

3. To make cheesecake filling: In a food processor, purée all cheesecake filling ingredients until very smooth. Pour into crust.

4. To make cashew filling: In a bowl, whisk together all cashew filling ingredients. Pour carefully over cheesecake layer in pie plate.

5. Bake in centre of oven for 30 to 35 minutes or until filling is almost set. It may rise up around the edges or even through the middle of the cashew filling. Cool pie on a wire rack. Serve either chilled or at room temperature.

PREP: About 15 mins.
BAKE: About 30 mins.

MAKES 12 SERVINGS

MAKE AHEAD
Bake this pie up to 1 day in advance and freeze for up to 1 month.

NUTRITIONAL ANALYSIS PER SERVING
290 calories
5.1 g protein
10 g fat, total
2.9 g fat, saturated
46 g carbohydrates
48 mg cholesterol
0.7 g fibre

TIP
To toast cashews, place in a skillet and cook on high for 2 minutes or until slightly browned.

lemon mousse pie

PREP: About 20 mins.
CHILL: About 2 h.

MAKES 12 SERVINGS

MAKE AHEAD
You can prepare this pie up
to 1 day in advance.

NUTRITIONAL ANALYSIS
PER SERVING
200 calories
4.2 g protein
5.7 g fat, total
1.7 g fat, saturated
33 g carbohydrates
5.8 mg cholesterol
0.7 g fibre

TIP
For convenience, buy egg
whites in containers (1 egg
white equals 2 tbsp liquid
egg whites).

A creamy lemon filling over a chocolate cookie crust is to die for. This pie is sensational and simple to make, and its mousse filling, unlike most, doesn't require 2 cups of whipping cream (which amounts to a lot of calories!).

CRUST
1-3/4 cups chocolate wafer crumbs
2 tbsp water
1 tbsp granulated sugar
1 tbsp vegetable oil

GARNISH
Grated lemon rind (optional)

MOUSSE
1-1/4 cup granulated sugar
1/2 cup smooth light ricotta cheese
2 oz light cream cheese, softened
1/3 cup fresh lemon juice
1 tbsp finely grated lemon rind
2 tsp unflavored gelatin powder
3 tbsp cold water

3 large egg whites
1/4 tsp cream of tartar

1. Spray a 9-inch pie plate with cooking spray.
2. To make crust: In a bowl, stir together crust ingredients just until crumbs come together. Press onto bottom and side of prepared pie plate.
3. To make mousse: In a food processor, purée 3/4 cup of the sugar with the ricotta cheese, cream cheese, lemon juice, and lemon rind until smooth.
4. In a small microwave-safe bowl, combine gelatin and water. Let stand for 2 minutes; microwave on High for 20 seconds. Stir until gelatin dissolves. With food processor running, add gelatin mixture to ricotta mixture through feed tube. Transfer mixture to a large bowl.
5. In another bowl, beat egg whites with cream of tartar until foamy. Gradually add remaining sugar, beating until stiff peaks form. Stir one-quarter of the egg whites into the ricotta mixture. Gently fold in remaining egg whites just until blended. Spoon mixture into crust. Chill for 2 hours or until filling is set firm. Serve garnished with additional lemon rind (if using).

marble mocha cheesecake

When I was having my food products produced and sold in stores, this cheesecake was one of the hottest-selling items. (I purchased some myself and stored it in the freezer!) Try this one: it's outstanding.

CRUST
2-1/4 cups chocolate wafer crumbs
2-1/2 tbsp water
1 tbsp vegetable oil

FILLING
1-1/2 cups smooth light ricotta cheese
4 oz light cream cheese, softened
1-1/4 cups granulated sugar
3/4 cup low-fat sour cream
2 eggs
2 tbsp all-purpose flour
2 tsp instant coffee dissolved in 1 tbsp hot water

MARBLE
2 tbsp semi-sweet chocolate chips
2 tsp water

1. Preheat oven to 350°F. Spray a 9-inch springform pan with cooking spray.
2. To make crust: In a bowl, stir together all crust ingredients. Press onto bottom and partway up side of prepared pan.
3. To make filling: In a food processor, purée all filling ingredients until smooth. Pour into crust.
4. To make marble: In a small microwave-safe bowl, heat chocolate with water on High in the microwave for 20 seconds. Stir until smooth. Drizzle over cheesecake; using a knife, marble the batter.
5. Bake in centre of oven for 40 to 45 minutes or just until centre of cheesecake is still slightly loose. Cool on a wire rack to room temperature. Refrigerate for 2 hours or until chilled.

PREP: About 15 mins.
BAKE: About 40 mins.

MAKES 12 SERVINGS

MAKE AHEAD
This cheesecake can be baked up to 2 days in advance or frozen for up to 2 months.

NUTRITIONAL ANALYSIS PER SERVING
285 calories
8.3 g protein
9.3 g fat, total
4 g fat, saturated
43 g carbohydrates
53 mg cholesterol
0.8 g fibre

TIP
When it comes to baking, instant coffee gives a more intense flavor than brewed coffee. I always make quite strong instant coffee for baking.

new york–style cheesecake

PREP: About 15 mins.
BAKE: About 35 mins.

MAKES 12 SERVINGS

MAKE AHEAD
You can make the cheesecake
up to 1 day ahead or make
and freeze—without the
berries—for up to 1 month.

NUTRITIONAL ANALYSIS
PER SERVING
223 calories
7 g protein
7 g fat, total
2.6 g fat, saturated
33 g carbohydrates
31 mg cholesterol
0.6 g fibre

TIP
To make crumbs from vanilla
wafers, process them in a
food processor until crumbly.

Remember Carnegie Deli New York Cheesecake? The piece that could serve six people? Well, at something like 960 calories and more than 50 grams of fat a slice, it is hard to forget. Here's my much healthier version that's so creamy you'll never believe the calorie count.

CRUST
2 cups vanilla wafer or graham cracker crumbs
2-1/2 tbsp water
2 tbsp granulated sugar
1 tbsp vegetable oil

FILLING
1-2/3 cups smooth light ricotta cheese
3 oz light cream cheese, softened
3/4 cup granulated sugar
1/3 cup low-fat plain yogurt
1 egg
1-1/2 tbsp all-purpose flour
2 tsp fresh lemon juice
1 tsp vanilla

GLAZE
2 tbsp strawberry or apple jelly

GARNISH
Berries and/or sliced fresh fruit

1. Preheat oven to 350°F. Spray an 8-inch springform pan with cooking spray.
2. To make crust: In a bowl, stir together all crust ingredients until blended. Press onto bottom and partway up side of prepared pan.
3. To make filling: In a food processor or blender, purée all filling ingredients until smooth. Pour into crust.
4. Bake in centre of oven for 35 to 40 minutes or just until centre of cheesecake is still slightly loose. Cool on a wire rack to room temperature. Refrigerate for 2 hours or until chilled.
5. To make glaze: Melt jelly in microwave for 20 seconds. Decorate cheesecake with berries or sliced fruit. Brush glaze over top.

carrot cake with cream cheese frosting

Carrot cake must be one of the most popular cakes around, but the traditional version is loaded with calories and fat. My variation uses oil, fruit, and yogurt to lessen the fat content.

CAKE

1/3 cup vegetable oil

1 cup granulated sugar

2 large eggs

1 tsp vanilla

1 medium ripe banana, mashed

1-1/2 cups grated carrots

1/2 cup raisins

1/3 cup canned crushed pineapple, drained

1/3 cup low-fat plain yogurt

1/4 cup toasted coconut

1-3/4 cups all-purpose flour

1-1/2 tsp baking powder

1 tsp baking soda

1-1/2 tsp cinnamon

1/4 tsp ground nutmeg

FROSTING

1 cup icing sugar

1 cup smooth light ricotta cheese

3 cup light cream cheese, softened

GARNISH

2 tbsp toasted coconut

1. Preheat oven to 350°F. Spray two 9-inch round cake pans with cooking spray.
2. To make cake: In a large bowl and using an electric mixer, beat oil and sugar until smooth. Beat in eggs and vanilla (mixture may look curdled). Using a wooden spoon, stir in banana, carrots, raisins, pineapple, yogurt, and coconut until well combined. In another bowl, stir together flour, baking powder, baking soda, cinnamon, and nutmeg. Stir flour mixture into carrot mixture just until moistened. Divide mixture between prepared pans.
3. Bake in centre of oven for 20 to 25 minutes or until a tester inserted in centre of cake comes out clean. Cool in pans on a wire rack for 10 minutes. Invert cakes onto a wire rack to cool completely.
4. To make frosting: In a food processor or in a bowl and using an electric mixer, beat icing sugar, ricotta, and cream cheese until smooth. Chill while cake is baking.
5. Place a cake on a serving platter. Spread some frosting over top. Top with remaining cake; spread frosting over top and side of cake. Sprinkle top with toasted coconut.

PREP: About 15 mins.
BAKE: About 20 mins.

MAKES 14 SERVINGS

MAKE AHEAD
This cake can be baked up to 2 days in advance or frozen for up to 2 months.

NUTRITIONAL ANALYSIS PER SERVING
282 calories
4.5 g protein
10 g fat, total
4.2 g fat, saturated
45 g carbohydrates
37 mg cholesterol
1.9 g fibre

TIPS
Ripe unpeeled bananas can be kept frozen for up to 1 year. Raisins can be replaced with dried cranberries or chopped dates (pitted), apricots, or prunes. You can use a food processor to mix the batter, but take care not to over-process it. Toast coconut in a skillet on high for 2 minutes or until just lightly browned.

lemon pound cake

PREP: About 15 mins.
BAKE: About 45 mins.

MAKES 12 SERVINGS

MAKE AHEAD
This pound cake can be baked
1 day in advance or frozen for
up to 1 month.

NUTRITIONAL ANALYSIS
PER SERVING
241 calories
4.5 g protein
7.6 g fat, total
1.9 g fat, saturated
40 g carbohydrates
42 mg cholesterol
0.6 g fibre

TIP
Soften the cream cheese for
easier mixing.

In my first light cookbook, I created a recipe called Lemon Loaf Cake that drew raves from everyone who tried it. This pound cake has a twist: a lemon cream cheese frosting.

CAKE
2 eggs
1-1/4 cups granulated sugar
1/4 cup fresh lemon juice
1/4 cup vegetable oil
2 oz light cream cheese, softened
1 tbsp grated lemon rind
1 tbsp poppyseeds
1-2/3 cups all-purpose flour
1-1/2 tsp baking powder
1/2 tsp baking soda
2/3 cup low-fat sour cream

ICING
1 oz light cream cheese, softened
1/2 cup icing sugar
1 tbsp fresh lemon juice

GARNISH
Poppyseeds and/or grated lemon rind

1. Preheat oven to 350°F. Spray a 9- × 5-inch loaf pan with cooking spray.
2. To make cake: In a food processor or in a large bowl and using an electric mixer, beat eggs, sugar, lemon juice, oil, cream cheese, lemon rind, and poppyseeds until smooth. In another bowl, stir together flour, baking powder, and baking soda; into cream cheese mixture, alternately stir flour mixture and sour cream, making three additions of each. Pour into prepared pan.
3. Bake in centre of oven for 45 to 50 minutes or until a tester inserted in centre of cake comes out clean. Remove from pan and cool completely on a wire rack.
4. To make icing: In a food processor or in a bowl and using an electric mixer, beat all icing ingredients together. Spread over top of cake. Garnish with poppyseeds and/or lemon rind.

banana date coffee cake

The combination of ripe bananas and dates is exceptional. The yogurt is a substitute for oil and is what gives this cake its moisture.

CAKE

2 medium ripe bananas, mashed

1 egg

1 egg white

1 cup granulated sugar

1/3 cup vegetable oil

2 tsp vanilla

1-3/4 cup all-purpose flour

1-1/2 tsp baking powder

1/2 tsp baking soda

2/3 cup low-fat plain yogurt

1 cup chopped pitted dates

FILLING

2/3 cup packed brown sugar

1 tsp cinnamon

1. Preheat oven to 350°F. Spray a 9-inch springform pan with cooking spray.
2. To make cake: In a bowl and using an electric mixer, beat together bananas, egg, egg white, granulated sugar, oil, and vanilla until well mixed. In another bowl, stir together flour, baking powder, and baking soda; into banana mixture alternately stir flour mixture and yogurt, making several additions of each. Fold in dates.
3. To make filling: In a small bowl, stir together brown sugar and cinnamon.
4. Pour half of batter into prepared pan. Sprinkle with half of filling. Pour remaining batter over top. Sprinkle with remaining filling.
5. Bake in centre of oven for 35 to 40 minutes or just until a tester inserted in centre of cake comes out clean. Cool in pan on a wire rack.

PREP: About 15 mins.
BAKE: About 35 mins.

MAKES 14 SERVINGS

MAKE AHEAD
You can bake this cake up to 1 day in advance or freeze for up to 2 weeks.

NUTRITIONAL ANALYSIS
PER SERVING
250 calories
3.4 g protein
5.7 g fat, total
0.4 g fat, saturated
45 g carbohydrates
15 mg cholesterol
0.3 g fibre

TIP
I toss unpeeled ripe bananas into the freezer. Defrost before using in recipes. To cut dates, use scissors sprayed with vegetable oil.

mocha chocolate chip crumb cake

PREP: About 15 mins.
BAKE: About 35 mins.

MAKES 14 SERVINGS

MAKE AHEAD
This cake can be baked 1 day
in advance or baked and
frozen for up to 1 month.

NUTRITIONAL ANALYSIS
PER SERVING
262 calories
4.5 g protein
8.7 g fat, total
2.2 g fat, saturated
41 g carbohydrates
34 mg cholesterol
1.3 g fibre

TIP
You can always substitute
white, mint, or milk chocolate
chips.

One of my favorite cakes was the chocolate chip crumb cake that had a white batter, chocolate chips, and a brown sugar cinnamon streusel filling. That recipe has been loved by so many I decided to modify it. Now, the cake is chocolate.

CAKE
2 eggs
1-1/3 cups granulated sugar
3/4 cup smooth light ricotta cheese
1/3 cup vegetable oil
2 tsp instant coffee dissolved in 1 tbsp water
1-1/4 cups all-purpose flour
1/3 cup unsweetened cocoa powder
2 tsp baking powder
1/2 tsp baking soda
3/4 cup low-fat plain yogurt
1/3 cup semi-sweet chocolate chips

FILLING
3/4 cup packed brown sugar
4 tsp unsweetened cocoa powder

1. Preheat oven to 350°F. Spray a 9-inch Bundt pan with cooking spray.
2. To make cake: In a food processor, purée eggs, sugar, ricotta, oil, and dissolved coffee until smooth. In a bowl, stir together flour, cocoa, baking powder, and baking soda. Into ricotta mixture alternately stir flour mixture and yogurt, making three additions of each. Fold in chocolate chips.
3. To make filling: In a small bowl, combine filling ingredients.
4. Pour half of batter into prepared pan. Sprinkle with half of filling. Pour remaining batter over top. Sprinkle with remaining filling.
5. Bake in centre of oven for 35 minutes or until a tester inserted in centre of cake comes out clean. Cool in pan on a wire rack before inverting.

pear and dried cranberry sour cream coffee cake

Coffee cakes are simple, delicious cakes to have any time of day, but this one is in a league of its own. Serve it when entertaining.

PREP: About 15 mins.
BAKE: About 40 mins.

MAKES 16 SERVINGS

MAKE AHEAD
Bake up to 1 day in advance or bake and freeze for up to 1 month.

NUTRITIONAL ANALYSIS PER SERVING
248 calories
3.5 g protein
7.8 g fat, total
0.8 g fat, saturated
42 g carbohydrates
31 mg cholesterol
1.2 g fibre

TIP
If pears aren't available, substitute apples, peaches, or plums. If the fruit isn't ripe, double the sugar in the fruit mixture.

TOPPING
1/3 cup packed brown sugar
3 tbsp chopped toasted pecans
1-1/2 tbsp all-purpose flour
2 tsp margarine or butter
1/2 tsp cinnamon

PEAR MIXTURE
2 cups chopped peeled ripe pears
1/2 cup dried cranberries
1 tbsp granulated sugar
1 tsp cinnamon

CAKE
2/3 cup packed brown sugar
1/2 cup granulated sugar
1/3 cup vegetable oil
2 large eggs
1 tbsp grated orange rind
2 tsp vanilla

1-2/3 cups all-purpose flour
2 tsp baking powder
1 tsp baking soda
1/2 cup orange juice
1/2 cup low-fat sour cream

1. Preheat oven to 350°F. Spray a 10-inch springform pan with cooking spray.
2. To make topping: In a small bowl, combine topping ingredients until crumbly.
3. To make pear mixture: In a bowl, stir together all pear mixture ingredients.
4. To make cake: In a large bowl and using a whisk or an electric mixer, beat together sugars and oil. Beat in eggs one at a time, beating well after each addition. Beat in orange rind and vanilla. In a separate bowl, stir together flour, baking powder, and baking soda. In another bowl, stir together orange juice and sour cream. Using a wooden spoon, into sugar mixture alternately stir flour mixture and sour cream mixture; stir in pear mixture. Spoon batter into prepared pan. Sprinkle with topping
5. Bake in centre of oven for 40 to 45 minutes or until a tester inserted in centre of cake comes out clean. Cool in pan on a wire rack.

brownie fudge layer cake

PREP: About 15 mins.
BAKE: About 15 mins.

MAKES 14 SERVINGS

MAKE AHEAD
Bake up to 2 days in advance
or bake and freeze with icing
for up to 2 months.

NUTRITIONAL ANALYSIS
PER SERVING
240 calories
3.4 g protein
6.8 g fat, total
1.8 g fat, saturated
43 g carbohydrates
19 mg cholesterol
1.6 g fibre

TIP
To make it easy to pour corn
syrup from a measuring cup,
first spray the cup with
vegetable oil.

You can tell that I love chocolate desserts. This one is a combination of a brownie and cake, and is moist and delicious.

ICING
1-1/3 cups icing sugar
1 cup smooth light ricotta cheese
2 oz light cream cheese, softened
2 tbsp unsweetened cocoa powder

GARNISH
Icing sugar or 1 tbsp flaked chocolate

CAKE
1/4 cup semi-sweet chocolate chips
2 tbsp water
1 cup granulated sugar
1/2 cup unsweetened cocoa powder
1 large egg
2 large egg whites
3/4 cup low-fat sour cream
1/2 cup golden corn syrup
1/4 cup vegetable oil
2 tsp vanilla
1-1/4 cups all-purpose flour
1-1/2 tsp baking powder

1. To make icing: In a small food processor or in a bowl and using a whisk or an electric mixer, beat all icing ingredients until smooth. Chill while preparing cakes.
2. Preheat oven to 350°F. Spray two 9-inch round cake pans with cooking spray.
3. To make cake: In a small microwave-safe bowl, heat chocolate chips and water on High in the microwave for 30 seconds or just until chips begin to melt. Stir until smooth. In a large bowl and using a whisk or an electric mixer, beat together chocolate mixture, sugar, cocoa, egg, egg whites, sour cream, corn syrup, oil, and vanilla. In another bowl, stir together flour and baking powder. With a wooden spoon, stir flour mixture into chocolate mixture just until combined. Divide between prepared pans.
4. Bake in centre of oven for 15 to 20 minutes or until a tester inserted in centre of cake comes out clean. Cool in pans for 10 minutes on a wire rack. Invert cakes onto a wire rack to cool completely.
5. Place one cake on a serving platter. Spread some icing over top. Top with remaining cake; spread icing over top and side of cake. Sprinkle with icing sugar or flaked chocolate.

old-fashioned date squares

Date squares, often known as matrimonial squares, have been a classic for decades. The oatmeal crust often contains a cup or more of butter or vegetable shortening. My version uses only 1/3 cup oil mixed with water, and the squares are still incredibly delicious and rich tasting.

1-1/2 cups chopped pitted dates (8 oz)
1/4 cup granulated sugar
1-1/4 cups water
1-1/4 cups quick-cooking oats
1 cup all-purpose flour
3/4 cup packed brown sugar
1/3 cup vegetable oil
1/4 cup chopped toasted pecans
1/2 tsp cinnamon

1. In a saucepan, combine dates, sugar, and 1 cup of the water. Bring to a boil; reduce heat to medium, and cook for 15 minutes or until dates are soft and liquid is absorbed. Mash mixture and let it cool.
2. Preheat oven to 350°F. Spray an 8-inch square baking dish with cooking spray.
3. In a bowl, stir together remaining ingredients, including remaining 1/4 cup of water, until combined. Press half onto bottom of prepared dish. Spread cooled date mixture over top. Sprinkle remaining oat mixture on top of dates.
4. Bake in centre of oven for 25 minutes or until top is golden. Cool in pan on a wire rack.

PREP: About 20 mins.
COOK: About 25 mins.

MAKES 16 SERVINGS

MAKE AHEAD
Make up to 2 days in advance. Freeze for up to 2 months.

NUTRITIONAL ANALYSIS PER SERVING
211 calories
2.4 g protein
6.4 g fat, total
0.5 g fat, saturated
36 g carbohydrates
0 mg cholesterol
2.1 g fibre

TIP
Buy dried foods in bulk and freeze them. You can chop dates easily with scissors sprayed with vegetable oil. Toast pecans by cooking in a small skillet on high heat for 3 minutes or until lightly browned.

PREP: About 5 mins.
BAKE: About 15 to 20
mins.

MAKES 12 SERVINGS

MAKE AHEAD
These are great baked 1 day
in advance and will keep
frozen for up to 1 month.

NUTRITIONAL ANALYSIS
PER SERVING
140 calories
2.3 g protein
7 g fat, total
1.5 g fat, saturated
20 g carbohydrates
19 mg cholesterol
1.2 g fibre

TIP
The key to great brownies is
not to overmix or overbake
them. Brownies should
always be moist (slightly wet)
in the middle when taken out
of the oven.

triple chocolate brownies

I created this recipe for the Mövenpick restaurants in Toronto. These restaurants sold more than 1,500 of these brownies per month not only because they're delicious, but also because they're lighter than other brownies.

BROWNIES
2/3 cups sugar
1/4 cup vegetable oil
1 egg
1 tsp vanilla
1/3 cup unsweetened cocoa powder
1/3 cup all-purpose flour
1 tsp baking powder
1/4 cup low-fat yogurt or sour cream
1/4 cup semi-sweet chocolate chips

ICING
2 oz light cream cheese
2/3 cup icing sugar
1-1/2 tsp cocoa powder
1-1/2 tsp water

1. Preheat oven to 350°F. Spray an 8-inch square metal pan with cooking spray.
2. To make brownies: In a bowl, combine sugar, oil, egg, and vanilla until well mixed. Add cocoa; mix well. Add flour, baking powder, yogurt, and chocolate chips, mixing just until combined and smooth. Don't overmix.
3. Pour batter into pan; bake in centre of oven for 15 to 20 minutes just until set. Do not overbake. Cool.
4. To make icing: In a blender or food processor, blend icing ingredients until smooth. Spread over brownie batch. Cut into squares.

banana chocolate chip muffins

super
quick

Coffee shop muffins are definitely high in calories and fat—many have as many as 550 calories and 30 grams of fat! This muffin recipe using mashed bananas and yogurt requires far less oil.

3/4 cup mashed ripe bananas (about 1-1/2 medium bananas)
1/2 cup granulated sugar
1/4 cup vegetable oil
1 egg
1 tsp vanilla
1 cup all-purpose flour
1 tsp baking powder
1 tsp baking soda
1/2 cup low-fat plain yogurt or low-fat sour cream
1/4 cup semi-sweet chocolate chips

1. Preheat oven to 375°F. Spray a 12-cup muffin pan with cooking spray.
2. In a large bowl and using an electric mixer, beat together bananas, sugar, oil, egg, and vanilla until well mixed. In another bowl, stir together flour, baking powder, and baking soda; stir flour mixture into banana mixture. Stir in yogurt. Fold in chocolate chips. Divide among prepared muffin cups.
3. Bake in centre of oven for 15 minutes or until a tester inserted in centre of muffins comes out clean.

PREP: About 5 mins.
BAKE: About 15 mins.

MAKES 12 SERVINGS

MAKE AHEAD
Make these 1 day in advance or freeze for up to 2 months.

NUTRITIONAL ANALYSIS
PER SERVING
150 calories
2 g protein
6 g fat, total
1.2 g fat, saturated
21 g carbohydrates
18 mg cholesterol
1 g fibre

TIP
I freeze ripe bananas, with the skin on, for months. Defrost at room temperature or in the microwave on High for 1 minute.

chocolate chip vanilla biscotti

Biscotti are my favorite cookie: I dip them in my coffee or have one as a light, low-fat snack.

PREP: About 10 mins.
BAKE: About 40 mins.

MAKES 30 SERVINGS

MAKE AHEAD
These cookies can be stored in an airtight container for up to 2 weeks or frozen for up to 2 months.

NUTRITIONAL ANALYSIS
PER SERVING
92 calories
0.1 g protein
2.6 g fat, total
0.5 g fat, saturated
16 g carbohydrates
6.6 mg cholesterol
0.3 g fibre

TIP
For convenience, buy egg whites in a container. Two egg whites is equivalent to 1/4 cup liquid egg whites.

3/4 cup granulated sugar
1/2 cup packed brown sugar
1/4 cup vegetable oil
1 egg
2 egg whites
1 tbsp vanilla
1/8 tsp salt
2 cups all-purpose flour
2 tsp baking powder
1/3 cup semi-sweet chocolate chips

1. Preheat oven to 350°F. Spray a baking sheet with cooking spray.
2. In a bowl and using an electric mixer, beat sugars, oil, egg, egg whites, vanilla, and salt. In another bowl and using a wooden spoon, stir together flour, baking powder, and chocolate chips. Combine flour mixture with sugar mixture, stirring until combined. Divide mixture in half. Using slightly wet hands, form each half into a 12- × 3-inch log; place on prepared baking sheet, spacing logs well apart.
3. Bake in centre of oven for 20 minutes. Cool for 5 minutes. With a serrated knife, cut logs into 1/2-inch slices. Lying them flat, return slices to baking sheet and bake another 20 minutes or until crisp. Cool on a wire rack.

subject index

recipe index